# Imprints 11

## VOLUME I

P9-DER-895

### Short Stories
### Poetry

Dom Saliani
David Friend

CONSULTANT
Marg Frederickson

GAGE EDITORIAL TEAM
Joe Banel
Diane Robitaille
Cathy Zerbst

 EDUCATIONAL PUBLISHING COMPANY
A DIVISION OF CANADA PUBLISHING CORPORATION
Vancouver · Calgary · Toronto · London · Halifax

Copyright © 2001 Gage Learning Corporation
Thomson Nelson
1120 Birchmount Road
Toronto, Ontario  M1K 5G4
1-800-668-0671
www.nelson.com

All rights reserved. No part of this work covered by the copyrights hereon may be reproduced or used in any form or by any means—graphic, electronic, electrostatic, or mechanical—without the prior written permission of the publisher or, in the case of photocopying or other reprographic copying, a licence from the Canadian Copyright Licensing Agency.

Any request for photocopying, recording, taping, or information storage and retrieval systems of any part of this book shall be directed in writing to the Canadian Copyright Licensing Agency, One Yonge Street, Ste. 1900, Toronto, ON  M5E 1E5.

Permissions Editor: Elizabeth Long
Photo Research: Karen Taylor
Design, Art Direction, & Electronic Assembly: Wycliffe Smith Design Inc.
Cover Image: Dave Robertson/Masterfile

ISBN-13: 978-0-7715-0941-4
ISBN-10: 0-7715-0941-3

National Library of Canada cataloguing in publication data

Main entry under title:

Imprints 11

For use in grade 11.
Issued also in 1 vol.
Contents: v. 1. Short stories and poetry / [compiled by] Dom Saliani, Jeff Siamon.
ISBN 0-7715-0941-3

1. Readers (Secondary).  I. Saliani, Dom.

PE1121.I536 2001a          428'.6          C2001-930047-6

The selections collected in *Imprints* are drawn from a wide variety of sources. To respect the integrity of these sources, Gage has preserved the original spelling, grammar, and punctuation used by each author. Gage editorial style, however, is used throughout for activities and other text generated by Gage writers.

ISBN 0-7715-0941-3
2 3 4 5 FP 09 08 07 06
Printed and bound in Canada

## IMPRINTS REVIEWERS

Patricia Ames, Rainbow DB, ON

Gerry Bartlett, School District #2, NB

Mike Budd, Greater Essex County DSB, ON

Michelle Coleman, Cape Breton Victoria Regional SB, NS

Kathy Coles, Langley SB, BC

Jennifer Connell, Eastern School District, PEI

Maria DeBerardinis, Dufferin-Peel Roman Catholic DSB, ON

Bryan Ellefson, Palliser Regional Schools, AB

Pat Kover, Calgary B of E, AB

Karen Montgomery-Jones, Algoma DSB, ON

Jane Prosser, Saskatoon B of E, SK

Catherine Reid, Avalon East SB, NF

Robert Riel, Winnipeg School Division #1, MB

Shelley Robinson, Rocky View School Div. #41, AB

Georgina Barbosa Tousignant, Dufferin-Peel RCSSB, ON

Harry Wagner, Parkland School Div. #70, AB


Gage would like to thank Marg Frederickson's Grade 12
students from Burnaby North Senior Secondary School for
their significant contributions.

# Table of Contents

## Short Stories

## Poetry

✦ indicates Canadian content

# Alternate Table of Contents

# Short Stories

Fiction is the truth inside the lie.
*Stephen King*

# Mirror Image

## By Lena Coakley

*The following story is divided into seven different sections. Identify the time periods dealt with in each. Does the story unfold in a linear or non-linear manner?*

I f only there were no mirrors, Alice sometimes thought, although she carried one in her backpack wherever she went. It was a silver-plated mirror her father had given her with the initials ACS on the back. Just you, Alice, she would say to herself, looking the way you've always looked. Then she'd pull out the mirror. The surprise and disbelief at seeing the reflection was a joke she played on herself over and over.

It was disquieting, however, to come upon a mirror without warning. She would say "excuse me" to her own reflection in shop windows. Mirrors in unexpected places would make her start and lose her nerve. She avoided the girls' bathroom altogether. Alice took to wearing sunglasses all the time, to remind herself, to keep something constantly in front of her eyes that would remind her that she looked different. Her teachers let her wear them. Maybe the word had come down from the top that she wasn't to be hassled for a while, but Alice thought it was more than that. She thought they were all a little afraid of her.

Of course her mind learned to ignore the glasses. The human mind is incredibly adaptable. Her mother was always telling her that.

"Do you think I move differently?" she asked her twin, Jenny, once identical. "Look how my feet kind of roll when I walk. And my hips, my hips feel totally different." Alice walked across the bedroom like a fashion model, wearing nothing but black bikini underwear. "Actually, as bodies go, this one is a lot better. I mean, check it out," Alice grabbed a chunk of her thigh, "no cellulite."

Jenny watched from inside her own body. "You looked okay before."

"Sorry, I didn't mean … You're pretty. I can see that now. But I never used to think that I was. You know, my old body used to weigh much less than this body weighs but I still wouldn't have been able to walk around naked in it. No one has ever told me that this body is ugly. For all I know it's never had zits. I haven't had one yet. I feel like I could do anything in this body. Hey, did I show you, I can almost touch my foot to the back of my head."

———

Alice had to re-learn how to move in the hospital, and to speak. At first the world was nothing but a mush of dark images, disconnected voices and prickly feelings all over her skin. If someone touched her arm she wasn't sure from which part of her body the sensation came. Colours seemed different. People's voices were pitched a tone higher. When she tried to speak she bit her tongue, which seemed enormous in her mouth and tasted funny. When she finally learned, the tone was different, but the inflections and the slight Maritime accent were the same. She'd had an accident, they said. But long before the psychiatrist told her, she knew. These weren't her hands. This wasn't her breath.

———

"Let me read your diary."

Alice and Jenny lay on top of their beds supposedly doing homework. Above each bed hung a charcoal portrait their father had drawn. He had finished them just before he died. Now, only Jenny's was a good likeness.

"Not now," said Jenny, closing the book and capping her ball point pen.

"You can read mine."

"I know what your diary says—Ooh, I found a new mole today on my new body. Ooh, don't my new armpits smell divine?"

"Come on. What do you have, some big secret in there? We've always read each other's diaries."

"I have to get to know you better." Jenny slipped her diary between her mattress and box spring.

"Yeah, right," Alice laughed. Then she realized her sister wasn't joking. "What, fourteen years wasn't enough?"

"You were in the hospital a long time, that's all I mean."

Alice swung her legs over the side of her bed and looked at Jenny. At one time looking at her was like looking in the mirror, and Alice still found her sister's coppery red hair and masses of freckles more familiar than her own reflection. "Jenny, we're still twins. I have the same memories: Camp Wasaga, moving to Toronto … Dad. You know, when I draw I can still make the shadows, just the way he showed us. Isn't that amazing? Even though I have a different hand. And my signature is the same too. This is me in here, Jenny. My brain is me."

Jenny rolled over on her bed. "Whatever. You still can't read it."

———

Alice was in the hospital for months. She saw doctors, interns, psychiatrists, physical therapists, speech therapists. Once a reporter, who had actually scaled the building, poked his head through the window to ask, "Hey, Alice, how do you feel?" and snapped a few photos.

All the mirrors had been removed, of course, from her room and bathroom, but Jenny and her mother brought the hand mirror with her initials when the doctors thought Alice was ready.

"They couldn't have saved your old body," her mother said. "This was the only way to keep you alive."

"No one knows what it will be like," said Jenny. "You're the only one who's ever survived before."

"I know all that," Alice slurred. The doctors had taken the precaution of giving her a mild sedative. It made her feel like everything was happening to someone else, far away. She held the silver mirror in one hand. With the other, she pulled at her face, squeezed it as if it were clay. Alice was mesmerized by the unfamiliar eyes, big and brown and dark. Whenever her father painted her he'd spend most of his time on the eyes. The eyes are the mirror of the soul, he used to say. Whose soul is that? Alice wondered. For a moment she considered screaming, but it was too much trouble. Besides, it wouldn't be her scream.

"It's okay, Mom," she said. "Maybe I'll start looking like myself again. If I try hard enough. If I concentrate hard enough. Very slowly, over the course of years, my eyes will change colour ... my face. It might ... "

Alice's mother stroked her hair. "We'll get through this," she said, "the human mind is incredibly adaptable."

---

"Mrs. Jarred's on TV again," Alice called.

"Turn it off," her mother said, "it's time for birthday cake," but Alice and Jenny kept watching. Above the television, the faces of the family portrait Alice's father had painted smiled out into the room.

"A new development in the story of Girl X," said the newscaster, "first surviving recipient of a brain transplant ... "

Alice's mother stood in the doorway wiping her hands on a tea towel. She had fewer freckles than Jenny, and the long braid which hung down her back wasn't quite so bright a red, but the family resemblance was unmistakable. "I don't want you to worry about the Jarreds, girls. My lawyer says they don't have a legal leg to stand on."

Mrs. Jarred, a middle-aged woman in a red checked coat, stood on a suburban lawn. She had dark hair just beginning to gray and Alice's large, dark eyes. A short man with a pot belly smiled self-consciously beside her.

"Is that your family?" Jenny asked.

"I don't even know them."

"Mrs. Jarred," said a female reporter with a microphone, "has science gone too far?"

"She's our daughter," the woman replied with emotion. "When we signed the release form donating her body, we didn't know they were going to bring her back to life with some new brain. Our Gail is alive and living somewhere in Toronto and I'm not even allowed to see her." Mrs. Jarred began to cry and the camera cut away to Alice and her mother leaving the hospital amid crowds of journalists. Since she was under eighteen, Alice's face was covered with a round, black dot. The girls had both seen this footage many times before.

"Gail. Wow. That's so weird."

"That's not my name."

The TV flashed pictures of the Jarreds before the accident. A girl with a dog. A smiling teenager wearing a party dress.

"Ooh, nice outfit, Gail."

"Darn those TV people," said Alice's mother. "They protect our privacy by not showing what you look like, and then they show pictures of your body before the accident. That makes a lot of sense."

"The Jarreds probably gave permission," said Alice. "Anyway, it doesn't matter. Everyone at school knows. The whole world knows."

Alice's mother continued as if she was talking to herself. "Those Jarreds ... If we start having reporters all over the lawn again ... " She twisted her face in disgust, strode across the room, and turned off the television with a sharp flick of her wrist.

"Hey."

"Come on, cake time. I made it from scratch. Alice's favourite, chocolate with mocha cream."

In the dining room a huge and elaborate cake was waiting on the table. Rich, white chocolate piping swirled over dark mocha. Ornate candy violets decorated the cake's tall sides.

"Awesome, Mom," said Alice. She couldn't remember her mother ever making a home-made cake before. "You blow first," she said to Jenny as she sat down. "You're the oldest."

"By two minutes," said Jenny, "and anyway, maybe I'm not the oldest anymore."

"What do you mean?"

"You might be older than me now with your new body. You might be old enough to drive for all we know."

Alice's brown eyes widened. "Mom, if my body is sixteen, does that mean I can get my license?"

"Forget it," her mother said as she lit the cake. "You could barely walk six months ago." She switched out the lights.

In the yellow glow of the candles Alice and Jenny followed a tradition that their father had started long ago. First Alice and her mother sang Happy Birthday to Jenny. Then, after Jenny had blown them out, the candles were lit again for Alice, and the song was sung a second time.

Alice blinked and squinted when the lights came on again. "I forgot to make a wish," she said.

Her mother smiled and handed a slice of the beautiful cake to each of the girls. "I guess you have to share your wish with Jenny."

Alice and Jenny laughed. One year, when they were little girls, the suggestion that they would have to share a wish sent them into fits of crying which their parents could only resolve by fitting the cake slices back into the cake and lighting the candles for a third and fourth time.

Alice cut the cake with the edge of her fork, happy that the tension brought on by the newscast had begun to melt away. She put a large bite into her mouth. Bitter. Alice tried hard to swallow, tried hard not to let her face show any reaction to the cake, but the taste of the mocha forced her mouth into a grimace. Jenny didn't miss it.

"I guess Gail doesn't like chocolate with mocha cream."

"No, it's good," said Alice, forcing it down.

Jenny pushed her own piece away. "I'm not hungry."

"Jeez, Jenny, why are you angry at me for not liking a piece of cake? I can't help it."

"Who's angry?"

"I have different taste buds now, and they're sending different messages to my brain. They're saying, this cake tastes gross. Sorry Mom."

"Okay," said Jenny. "You're always saying that you are still you because you have the same brain, but who is to say that your whole personality is in your head?"

"Where else would it be?"

"I don't know; maybe there was some other part of your body where part of your self lived. Maybe it was your big toe."

Alice's mother set down her fork. "Jenny, people have their big toes cut off and they're still themselves. People have heart transplants and they're still themselves."

"Right," said Alice. She smiled at her mother, but her mother looked away.

"Maybe not," Jenny said, "maybe they're a little bit different but they just don't notice. You're a lot different. You're a morning person.

You never see your old friends. You hang out with Imogen Smith and those snobs. Now you're going out for cheerleading, for goodness sake. And what is with those sunglasses? Sometimes … I don't know … Sometimes I think my sister is dead." Jenny pushed her chair back and ran out of the room.

Alice sat where she was, poking at her cake with her fork, trying not to cry.

Her mother got up and began to gather the plates. "I think," she began, her voice wavering, "I think cheerleading would be very good for your coordination."

Alice stared at her mother, but again her mother avoided her eyes. Suddenly Alice thought she understood the elaborate cake. She made it because she felt guilty, Alice thought, guilty for thinking, way down deep, that I'm not really the same daughter she knew before.

———

The first thing Alice saw when her eyes could focus was the white hospital ceiling, but the white had a slightly unnatural blueness to it, the way white looks on TV. Sometimes things were exquisitely clear and sharp, although she wasn't wearing her contacts, and she hadn't yet learned to ignore her eyelashes which seemed longer and darker than they had been before. When Alice saw her mother for the first time she cried and cried. Her skin had a different texture. Her hair hardly seemed red at all. She even had a different smell. And Jenny. Why was everyone she knew so different? Why wasn't her father there? Would he be different too?

———

When Alice met Mr. Jarred, it was in the middle of the street. A new sidewalk had just been poured on Bedford Avenue, so Alice had to walk in the street to go around the construction on the way home from school. A light rain was falling, preventing the concrete from setting. Mr. Jarred held an oversized umbrella, striped red and yellow, above his head. He might have walked right by her, but Alice was staring hard at him trying to remember something—anything—about him besides the newscast.

"Gail," he said in a soft mumble and then, "I'm sorry … I mean Alice … Do you know me?"

"I saw you on TV."

"Ah, yes." The two stood in silence for a moment.

"You should have an umbrella," he said. "This one's a ridiculous thing, my wife's. Here."

"No, no, it's just sprinkling, really," but Alice took the umbrella Mr. Jarred offered her, holding it upside down, its point in the road.

"This is very strange for me, very strange," he said, staring at her. "We knew you were in Toronto, but, well, to be honest, it was my wife who wanted to contact you. I … I thought it would be better not to see you. It's very strange," he repeated, then added, "You look so different."

"I do?"

"Your hair. The way you stand, even. Our Gail, she was an early bloomer, always slouched. Your accent is different too." He paused. "I understand, you know. My wife, she thinks our daughter is still alive, but I … I know." A car turned onto the street and honked at them. "I'd better go."

On impulse, Alice grabbed Mr. Jarred's hand. It was warm and big and rough and Alice knew she had never felt it before. "I knew I wouldn't remember you," she said, "but I was hoping, when you walked by, that I'd know you somehow."

Mr. Jarred took his hand away. "But you don't."

"No." Alice slid her dark glasses to the top of her head. "My dad—I guess you know he died in the accident."

"Yes."

"Sometimes I think if he were alive, he would just look into my eyes and know who was in here." The two stood in silence. Then Alice said, "What will you tell your wife?"

"I'll tell her," Mr. Jarred's voice began to falter, but he looked at her straight on, "I'll tell her I looked into your eyes and that I didn't see my daughter."

"I'm sorry," said Alice. She didn't ask the question that immediately came to her, but the words rang in her mind: who did you see?

Alice gripped the umbrella as she watched Mr. Jarred hurry around the corner. She stepped up to the curb and pressed her waist to the wooden barrier that protected the sidewalk. Then she folded the umbrella and secured the strap. In a small corner of the sidewalk she wrote her initials, ACS, with the tip of the umbrella.

Alice was here, she thought. And then she walked towards home.

**Lena Coakley** has published a number of other stories. Her short story "Mouse" placed second in *The Toronto Star's* Short Story Contest in 1999. She is currently working on a fantasy novel.

**I. Response**
**a.** The beginning of the story is deliberately written to create suspense. What questions are raised in the reader's mind by the end of the first two paragraphs? What are some possible answers for these questions?
**b.** Why does Jenny not allow her sister to read her diary? Do you agree with her reasoning? Explain.
**c.** Name some science fiction movies and/or stories you have previously encountered. Do you usually enjoy science fiction? Why or why not?

**2. Writing** *Diary Entry* At the end of the birthday party, Jenny says that she sometimes feels that her sister is dead. Imagine you are Jenny. Write a diary entry in which you explore why you feel this way.

**3. Media** *TV News Item* Alice says that a reporter scaled the hospital walls to get a picture and quotation from her. Why would a reporter go to such extremes to gain access to Alice? Why would Alice and her family want to avoid the media?

   With a partner, develop a 60-second TV news item that tells Alice's story. You could include an interview with Alice, her mother or sister, a doctor, or one of the Jarreds. Decide whether your item is going to be exploitative or respectful.

**4. Making Connections** In Lewis Carroll's classic book, *Alice's Adventures in Wonderland*, Alice undergoes a bewildering number of transformations—one moment she's the size of a mouse, the next she's a giant. During her adventures, she encounters a Caterpillar who raises a question often dealt with in literature:

> "Who are you?" said the Caterpillar.
> This was not an encouraging opening for a conversation. Alice replied, rather shyly, "I—I hardly know, Sir, just at present—at least I know who I was when I got up this morning, but I think I must have been changed several times since then."
> "What do you mean by that?" said the Caterpillar, sternly. "Explain yourself."

"I can't explain myself, I'm afraid, Sir," said Alice, "because I'm not myself, you see."

"I don't see," said the Caterpillar.

"I'm afraid I can't put it more clearly," Alice replied, very politely, "for I can't understand it myself, to begin with; and being so many different sizes in a day is very confusing."

"It isn't," said the Caterpillar.

"Well, perhaps you haven't found it so yet," said Alice; "but when you have to turn into a chrysalis— you will some day, you know—and then after that into a butterfly, I should think you'll feel it a little queer, won't you?"

"Not a bit," said the Caterpillar.

"Well, perhaps your feelings may be different," said Alice: "all I know is, it would feel very queer to me."

"You!" said the Caterpillar contemptuously. "Who are you?"

Which brought them back again to the beginning of the conversation.

Do you think it is helpful to draw a connection between Alice in "Mirror Image" and Alice in *Alice's Adventures in Wonderland*? Why or why not?

In a group, discuss the meaning of the term **allusion**. What do you think an author might gain by making an allusion to another story, especially one that is well known? Share your ideas with the class.

In a literary work, an **allusion** is a reference to another literary work, or a person, place, event, or object from history, literature, or mythology.

# The Prospector's Trail

By Cathy Jewison

"It's the old story. People been comin' to Yellowknife since the thirties, hoping to strike gold. Some make it, some don't."

"Noise! Traffic! Filth! Can't stand the commotion of the city, that's why I come out here," said the grizzled old guy. He leaned back in his lawn chair and stared at the campfire reflectively, taking a long pull of tea from a tin cup. The light from the flames glittered off his creased face and greying beard. The old-timer stared upwards. Norman and Jennifer followed his eyes, examining the dome of the northern night sky, which was still blue at nine-thirty p.m. They could hear a loon call from the nearby lake and the lap of the waves on the shore.

A grumble emanated from the far-off heavens. Thunder? No—the grumble grew into a growl and then into a roar, which gained intensity until it filled the air. Their eyes searched for the source of the clamour. Jennifer covered her ears. Then they saw it. A jetliner, glowing gold with the reflected light of the night sun, made an elegant curve over the city dump and moved in over Long Lake. It lined up with a runway and continued its descent, swooping across Highway 3 for a perfect landing at the Yellowknife airport.

"Flight 592 from Edmonton, right on schedule," Roy announced. He took another drink of tea. He winced.

"You know, when I invited you over for 'tea,' I actually meant we'd be drinking something stronger—you must be thirsty after your long drive. But all the beer's disappeared. Elsie must have had one of her damned card parties this afternoon, while I was out in the bush. And now all the peanuts are gone," he said, shaking the empty bag. "Elsie! *Elsie!*" he screamed towards an immense camper a few feet away. A tall, skinny woman came to the door. It was hard to see her features because an electric light was burning behind her.

"What?"

"We're out of peanuts."

"So go get some more. And get some beer while you're at it."

"You know I hate going into that damned city."

"I'm missing my show," she announced, slamming the door.

"Damned TV," he muttered towards the fire. "Supposed to be enjoying the beauties of nature. Get away from all that city stuff ..."

He continued on, but the rest of what he said was drowned out by the whine of a semitrailer zooming past on the highway a couple hundred yards behind them. He finished his diatribe about the same time the noise of the semi faded into the distance. He rooted in his tin cup with a grubby finger, then flicked something onto the ground.

"Skeeter," he stated. He turned to Norman.

"What kind of work you looking for?"

"Anything," Norman replied. "For now, anyway. I want to start a tourist operation. An interpretive centre—old buildings, dogsled rides in the winter, that sort of thing."

Roy nodded sagely.

"It's the old story. People been comin' to Yellowknife since the thirties, hoping to strike gold. Some did. Giant Mine's that way, Con's over there," he said, waving vaguely in opposite directions. "Then there's the others. Business tycoons. Government people. All want a piece of it. Some make it, some don't."

"Can't be any worse than southern Canada," Norman said.

Roy snorted.

"Bet you think differently when you're still living in a tent at forty below," he said.

Jennifer shuddered.

"Well, Yellowknife is the end of the road for me—and I don't mean just because the highway ends here," Norman said with a touch of bravado. "If I can't make it here, I can't make it anywhere."

"It's the end of the road for all true Yellowknifers. Place pulls a lot of people to it. The right ones stay."

"Any chance you could dig up something for us, Roy?" Jennifer asked.

"What do you mean?" the old-timer snapped. "What have you heard?"

"Nothing," Norman replied, jumping to his feet in alarm. His half-finished cup of tea, which had been balanced on his thigh, catapulted across the fire and hit Roy in the chest. The old man leaned forward and pulled the wet plaid flannel away from his skin.

"Good thing that wasn't hot," he observed. Jennifer stood up and strode away.

"Little missus gets a bit testy at times, eh? Know what that's like," Roy said, with a wink and a nod toward the camper. "I'd better pack it in—gotta rise and shine tomorrow," he added as he started to collect the tin cups.

Norman said goodnight and started off. Moments later, the old man heard a thud and turned to find Norman splayed on the ground.

"Tree root," he explained, hoisting himself upright and limping away.

"Watch your step, son," Roy said with a shake of his head.

Norman found Jennifer standing next to their tent, an artifact he'd bought at a garage sale in Winnipeg a couple of weeks earlier. It consisted of mildew and, to a lesser extent, of beige canvas.

"Get in," she commanded.

The tent came with an odd assortment of poles and guys that more or less kept everything in place. One of the poles was a bit too short, however, and if someone brushed against it, the tent collapsed. Since it was currently in its flattened state, Norman had to dive amongst the loose canvas and restore the poles. Jennifer then went around the outside, refastening guys. She gingerly crawled in. Norman was lying on top of his sleeping bag. Jennifer sat down on top of hers and shook her finger at him.

"Don't move for the rest of the night. Got it?"

"Got it."

Jennifer began to change into her pyjamas. The top was partway over her head when she was seized by convulsions. She gasped. She panted. Her shoulders jerked.

"Achoo!"

The tent rocked ominously. Jennifer sat perfectly still. As soon as she was certain the tent would remain upright, she popped her head through her pyjama top. She glared at Norman through the dim light.

"You realize I'm allergic to this damned thing."

"It's all we can afford."

"No kidding," she muttered.

"You shouldn't be so hard on people."

"It's not my fault I'm allergic," she replied, blowing her nose.

"I meant Roy. I think he can help us."

"I know he can—that camper's brand new."

"Don't push too hard, or you'll scare him away."

Jennifer finished pulling on her pyjama bottoms, then carefully tossed her clothes towards the few inches of floor at the foot of her sleeping bag.

"You'll never get ahead by pussyfooting around," she said.

"We'll just have to give it some time."

Jennifer sneezed again. She wiped her nose. She turned to her husband.

"I'll give it six weeks," she said. "Until Labour Day."

"That's not much time to start a new life."

"Norman. We're living in a tent. This is not a life."

"We've only been here a few hours and we're already accumulating authentic northern experience."

"That's what you call drinking tea with that old guy? Authentic northern experience?"

"He's a character. Local colour. It'll be important when I set up the interpretive centre. Maybe I can get him to work there."

"If you can get something useful out of him, fine. But keep your distance while you're doing it. I don't want you playing the role of hillbilly—trying to out-northern the northerners for the sake of your 'interpretive centre.' You're going to be the owner, so you'll have to show some decorum. Besides, you're lucky you didn't scald him. Like before."

"That was an accident."

"It's always an accident."

Norman sighed.

"Six weeks!" Jennifer snapped. "Unless I catch you wearing a red plaid flannel shirt, in which case I'll leave you on the spot."

She climbed into her sleeping bag and turned her back on her husband. Norman heard her sniffling well into the night. He wasn't sure if she was crying, or just needed an antihistamine. It could be hard to tell with Jennifer.

Norman and Jennifer had arrived at Fred Henne Territorial Park, located on the outskirts of Yellowknife, about suppertime that day. It was, indeed, the end of a long road for them. A year earlier, they had received their tourism studies certificates at a college in Winnipeg, then promptly got married. Norman still couldn't believe it—Jennifer had been a star student throughout the program, and he'd been flattered when she consented to date him because she liked his sense of whimsy.

With a sharp mind and an eye for the big picture, Jennifer was a whiz at developing tourism marketing programs. Norman's first love was interpretation—dressing up and acting like historical personages for the entertainment and edification of tourists. Jennifer's appreciation of his sense of whimsy had evaporated, however. She'd decided interpretation was undignified and convinced him to get into the corporate side of the industry. Norman found a decent job shortly after graduation, but was unnerved by the formality and high expectations of the office. Plagued by insomnia, he had become clumsy. His boss had laughed when Norman tripped on the carpet in the waiting room and landed face first in the fish tank. He had been less amused when Norman spilled a glass of Beaujolais on a client's silk dress. He was livid when Norman gave another client second-degree burns by dumping a pot of coffee on him. Norman's reputation spread and he could no longer get work. Jennifer became the sole breadwinner, but as a recent graduate, she couldn't earn enough to support them both. Jennifer half-heartedly agreed to let Norman pursue his dream of opening an interpretive centre, on the condition that he did it far away from anyone they knew. They scraped together a few hundred dollars, loaded their sparse belongings into Norman's battered Chevy van, and headed north.

The morning after their arrival, Norman walked by Roy's camping spot, where he found the old man seated at a concrete picnic table. He was wearing tattered work pants and a murky T-shirt, his omnipresent red plaid flannel shirt draped over the ensemble. The tea stain from the previous night was lost in a patchwork of grease and dirt. Norman smoothed his own spotless rugby shirt, and adjusted his collar.

"Come have breakfast," Roy called. "Can't get Elsie out here. We're supposed to be enjoying nature and all she does is complain about the bugs. The simple life! That's what it's all about! Wanna Pop-Tart?"

"It's okay—I have some granola back at the tent," Norman replied, but he sat down anyway.

"Suit yourself," Roy conceded as he ripped open a package and took a big bite out of one of the pastries. "You're supposed to toast them, but we're roughing it, after all," he mumbled around the glob in his mouth. "Where's the little lady?"

"Gone into town to look for work."

"Why ain't you with her?"

"She said she wasn't ready to unleash me upon an unsuspecting population."

"I see her point."

Norman noticed a dark rock flecked with gold lying in the dirt. He kicked at it, but missed and jammed his toe into one of the table's concrete supports. He gasped. Roy leaned over and scooped up the rock. He examined it closely.

"Fool's gold," he announced, tossing it away.

"Are you a miner, Roy?"

"You bet. A little prospecting. A little mining."

"Mining pays well, doesn't it?"

"Well enough," he said. He cast a self-conscious look towards the shiny new camper. "Thought you were a big tourism entrepreneur."

"I need to build up a nest egg. I also need to get to know the place. Develop some authentic northern experience," Norman said. "I was hoping you could help me. I'd like to follow you around. To observe."

Roy looked grim.

"What are you going to do today?" Norman coaxed.

"Prospector's Trail, I suppose," Roy replied with some reluctance.

"Prospecting? Excellent! Can I come?"

"Son! You don't ask a lady her age, and you don't ask a prospector to show you where he's working," the old man said firmly.

"It's just that I wanted to use you as the role model for the interpretive centre," Norman said.

"Oh?"

"If you don't mind being famous, that is."

"Well, maybe I could help a bit. You can come with me this morning. But this morning only, hear? Better take some provisions with you," he said, tossing a foil pack of Pop-Tarts at Norman. "Just don't try to walk and chew at the same time."

Roy set out across the campground at a rapid pace, with Norman close behind. They soon reached a huge, uneven field of pre-Cambrian rock. Roy didn't slow down. Norman teetered after him, but managed to stay upright.

"What are those little footprints painted on the rock?" he asked when he finally caught up with the sure-footed Roy.

"Directions."

"This is a walking trail?"

"Of course. Didn't think I'd really show you where I prospect, do you?"

Norman looked as deflated as his mildewed tent.

"I'm willing to share general knowledge, though. See that pillow of grey rock over there?"

Norman walked to the spot.

"Run your fingers over the surface. Feel the bumps?"

Norman nodded.

"What do you see?"

"Brownish-red granules."

"Good. They're garnets."

"Wow," Norman observed quietly, bending closer to the rock to examine them.

They continued on in silence for some time, until they reached the tumbledown remains of a cabin. The skeleton of a bed frame, a rusted-out woodstove and a few pieces of decaying cutlery were scattered around.

"Reminds me of the shack I lived in when I moved up in the forties. Made of plywood and packing crates." Roy sighed wistfully.

"Elsie didn't mind?"

"Living in a shack? Of course she did. But she saw the potential of the place—and of me."

They later found a vein of white quartz that prospectors had blasted.

"Quartz is the key," Roy explained. "Find it, and you just might find gold. Time for a rest."

The old man sat cross-legged beside the mutilated rock and closed his eyes. The sky clouded over, and a breeze came up. Roy's red plaid shirt fluttered around him. He swayed with the wind. His breathing became slower and deeper. Norman cautiously ripped open his pouch of Pop-Tarts and nibbled a corner. Finding that it hit the spot, he gobbled both pastries in the packet. Then, exhausted after another sleepless night, Norman closed his eyes. He, too, swayed with the wind. He drifted off, but jerked himself awake just as his head started to topple towards the ancient and very hard rock. He started to worry about the old man.

"Roy," he whispered. There was no reaction, so he said it louder. "Roy!"

"What?"

"I thought you'd fallen asleep."

"Asleep! Ain't you ever seen anyone meditating, son?"

"Meditating?"

"I thought you were educated. You know—meditating. Getting into the zone. Becoming one with the earth. The earth don't give up her secrets too easily. You gotta get to know her on a personal level."

"Oh."

"Time to go," Roy blurted as he jumped to his feet. He completed the circuit of the trail, which led them back to the campground. "Nice spending the morning with you," he said. "Now I have to get on with business."

Norman wiped a couple of drops of moisture from his arm. Roy had been generous towards him, but Norman would prefer if he didn't spit while he talked. Roy turned away. A large drop hit Norman's face. Rain.

Norman sprinted towards his tent as the deluge began. Moments later, Roy heard a stomach-turning shriek. The old-timer found Norman staring at the sodden puddle of his so-called shelter.

"You can stay in your van," he suggested.

"It's full of boxes and furniture," Norman replied as he began to pace. "What was I thinking? This is never going to work. Jen's going to leave me. I have no money. I can't earn any. It's over." He stopped moving and stared at Roy. "It's all over," he repeated in disbelief.

"You're packing it in? Just like that?" Roy demanded. "No interpretive centre?"

"I'm sorry, Roy. No interpretive centre."

"Don't panic. I'll help you. Get in your van. We're going prospecting."

They stopped by the camper to pick up some gumboots. Roy instructed Norman to drive away from Yellowknife, but they hadn't travelled for more than a minute before the old man told him to turn down a wide, well-maintained road that led past an industrial building. They were heading for the city dump.

"What now?" Norman muttered.

"Right over there," Roy said.

Norman pulled up next to a row of a half-dozen vehicles. Roy climbed out of the van and slowly rambled amongst the hills of debris, his eyes locked on the ground. Every now and then he would bounce on an abandoned couch to test the springs, or lift up a piece of plywood to see what was underneath. Other people were wandering in a similar fashion, but Roy ignored them. He motioned to Norman to join him, but Norman couldn't bring himself to leave the van. He fidgeted with the knobs on the radio. Then he realized someone was peering through the back window. Norman got out.

"You going to dump that stuff, buddy?" asked a young man in ragged jeans and a grimy windbreaker.

"That's my furniture. Back off."

"Settle down. I can find better out here, anyway," he said as he stalked off.

Norman carefully locked the van, put on Roy's extra pair of gumboots and set out after his mentor, stepping cautiously so as not to do a face-plant in the mud. He found Roy digging in a pile of garbage, a battered television and some lengths of two-by-four stacked neatly beside him.

"I thought you hated the noise and traffic and filth of the city," Norman observed.

"This ain't the city," the old man replied, surprised Norman hadn't noticed. He paused to wipe the drizzle from his forehead with a grimy hanky, then continued to root in the mud. "Eureka!" he shouted, as he extracted a dirty orange tarpaulin with a long rip in it. "Can I read 'em, or what?"

"What's it for?"

"It's for you. A fly for your tent. We'll wash it in the lake. Patch it with a little duct tape. Good as new!" he said gleefully. He examined Norman's face. "What's with you, boy? I thought you wanted to accumulate authentic northern experiences, and here you've been missin' one of the most authentic of them all."

"Can we go prospecting now?" Norman asked with as much patience as he could muster.

Roy beamed at him.

"Oh, no! This is how you made your money?" Norman demanded. "Prospecting and mining. At the dump?"

"After the first few years there was so much competition in the bush that I decided to use my skills here. You'd be amazed what you find. Take it home, clean it up, sell it. Got so much now, I'm having trouble shifting it."

Norman's eyes misted over and his throat constricted, but the cause was neither the rain in his eyes nor the stench in his nose. The rubble he saw before him was more than just the detritus of the Yellowknife dump—it was the rubble of his future. Wifeless. Homeless. Hopeless. Suddenly, he bent over. He wasn't sure why, since he could see little through the blur of tears. He ran his fingers over a pile of mud. He felt a bump. He wiped his eyes on the back of his sleeve and examined the mound more closely. A point of brownish-red was poking through. He flicked at it with his finger. A little more red showed. He dug deeper. It was cloth. He grabbed it and pulled out a red plaid flannel shirt, much like Roy's. The old-timer whistled.

"Impressive," he said as he examined it. "One little rip, but otherwise, good as new." He held it close to Norman's chest. "It'll fit you perfectly. Let's see what else you can do. Try over there."

Roy pointed him towards the back of the dump and gave him a little push. Norman meandered through the piles. He saw a strip of white gleaming through the mud. He wiped at it with the shirt he had unearthed. Not quartz this time, but porcelain. It was an old bathtub, the kind with feet.

"Excellent," Roy said. "That'll get you a couple hundred dollars. If you refinish it, you can get more. I'll find some packing crates—we can use them as skids to drag it out of here. Good thing I took you on that walk. Sure got you into the zone."

Norman slumped on the side of the bathtub.

"Don't knock it, son. You have a gift. You're in your element. Do you realize you haven't fallen once since you been out here?"

It was true. Norman felt himself relaxing. He took a deep breath and promptly choked.

"You'll get used to it," Roy assured him.

Norman surveyed the terrain through the mist. He instinctively headed towards the edge of the landfill. He came around a hill of debris and found some freshly dumped computers.

"You've hit the mother lode!" Roy squealed.

Norman examined them. "Fool's gold," he announced.

"I thought computers were worth a fortune."

"Nope. Too old. Got a screwdriver?"

Roy searched the pockets of his work pants and produced a rather nice multitool. "Found it here last week," he explained.

Norman used his sleeve to wipe the rain from one of the computers, then removed the case and looked inside.

"You know about these things?" Roy asked him.

"A bit. I think this one's a 486. Might work if it hasn't taken on too much dirt and rain. Not high powered, but we can use them for parts, if nothing else."

"You know how to set up one of those web site things?"

"Yah. It's not so hard."

"A little e-commerce might move my inventory."

"Who's your market?" Norman asked skeptically.

"People who can't come to visit, but want authentic northern artifacts just the same. You can make a planter out of anything," he said with a wink.

Norman smiled.

"Your little lady's not going to like it. She's more upscale than my Elsie."

"You're right. She won't see the potential. But like I said—this is the end of the road for me."

The sun was shining again when Jennifer returned to the campground with news that she'd landed a job. She found Norman outside Roy's camper. He was seated at the concrete picnic table, surrounded by computer parts. Roy was peering eagerly over Norman's shoulder, which was clad in a red plaid flannel shirt. Jennifer gasped.

"I found it at the dump. Elsie washed it for me," Norman explained as he monkeyed with a partially assembled computer.

"Me and your boy are going into business together," Roy proclaimed. "First e-commerce, then the interpretive centre."

"I think I've got it," Norman announced, as he connected the computer to an extension cord that stretched from the camper. A puff of smoke rose into the air. The two men looked at each other.

"Planter," they sang in unison.

"Grab me another," Norman instructed Roy. Jennifer's eyes shifted to the computers stacked beside the table.

"Found them at the dump," Norman repeated, but this time he looked her straight in the eye. "You wouldn't believe the business potential out there."

It was midnight when Norman wandered over to the tent, now protected with the freshly patched orange tarp. His van was gone, and several boxes of his possessions were sitting outside the tent. She hadn't left a note. Norman sighed and crawled into the rickety tent. It swayed slightly but remained upright. He slept soundly for the first time in months.

**Cathy Jewison** is a short story writer from
Yellowknife, Northwest Territories, whose work has
appeared in the Canadian short fiction magazine, *Storyteller.*

**1. Response**

**a.** What did you do to avoid confusion and to differentiate among the characters in the opening paragraphs of the story? What other effective strategies could you have used?

**b.** Write a brief description of Roy's personality. Do the same for Norman and Jennifer. In each case, include specific lines from the story that illustrate the character traits you've described.

**c.** In your view, do the characters in "The Prospector's Trail" seem like real people? Did you detect any stereotypes? Explain.

**d.** There are two red plaid shirts in the story. What is their symbolic significance?

**2. Literature Studies** *Character*  Characters in stories can be dynamic or static. A *dynamic* character changes in some important way as a result of his or her experience, while a *static* character stays the same. In "The Prospector's Trail," which characters are dynamic and which are static? Give reasons for your conclusions.

**3. Language Conventions** *Unconventional Grammar*  Reread the dialogue in the story, searching for examples of flawed grammar in Roy's speech—things such as sentence fragments and unconventional verb forms. Why do you think the author has Roy speak in this way? Look at the dialogue in one of your own stories. Do your characters speak in a way that is appropriate for them?

**4. Oral Language** *Group Discussion*  Norman says, "Yellowknife is the end of the road for me.... If I can't make it here, I can't make it anywhere." In a group, discuss whether Norman is likely to "make it" in Yellowknife. Did Norman make a good decision when he chose to stay in the north? What is your evaluation of the decision Jennifer made? Have one group member present a summary of your discussion to the class.

It's not easy being a hero—as Walter Mitty discovers again, and again, and again.

# The Secret Life of
# Walter Mitty

By James Thurber

"We're going through!" The Commander's voice was like thin ice breaking. He wore his full-dress uniform, with the heavily braided white cap pulled down rakishly over one cold gray eye. "We can't make it, sir. It's spoiling for a hurricane, if you ask me." "I'm not asking you, Lieutenant Berg," said the Commander. "Throw on the power lights! Rev her up to 8,500! We're going through!" The pounding of the cylinders increased: ta-pocketa-pocketa-pocketa-*pocketa-pocketa*. The Commander stared at the ice forming on the pilot window. He walked over and twisted a row of complicated dials. "Switch on No. 8 auxiliary!" he shouted. "Switch on No. 8 auxiliary!" repeated Lieutenant Berg. "Full strength in No. 3 turret!" shouted the Commander. "Full strength in No. 3 turret!" The crew, bending to their various tasks in the huge, hurtling eight-engined Navy hydroplane, looked at each other and grinned.

"The Old Man'll get us through," they said to one another. "The Old Man ain't afraid of Hell!"—

"Not so fast! You're driving too fast!" said Mrs. Mitty. "What are you driving so fast for?"

"Hmm?" said Walter Mitty. He looked at his wife, in the seat beside him, with shocked astonishment. She seemed grossly unfamiliar, like a strange woman who had yelled at him in a crowd. "You were up to fifty-five," she said. "You know I don't like to go more than forty. You were up to fifty-five." Walter Mitty drove on toward Waterbury in silence, the roaring of the SN202 through the worst storm in twenty years of Navy flying fading in the remote, intimate airways of his mind. "You're tensed up again," said Mrs. Mitty. "It's one of your days. I wish you'd let Dr. Renshaw look you over."

Walter Mitty stopped the car in front of the building where his wife went to have her hair done. "Remember to get those overshoes while I'm having my hair done," she said. "I don't need overshoes," said Mitty. She put her mirror back into her bag. "We've been all through that," she said, getting out of the car. "You're not a young man any longer." He raced the engine a little. "Why don't you wear gloves? Have you lost your gloves?" Walter Mitty reached in a pocket and brought out the gloves. He put them on, but after she had turned and gone into the building and he had driven on to a red light, he took them off again. "Pick it up, brother!" snapped a cop as the light changed, and Mitty hastily pulled on his gloves and lurched ahead. He drove around the streets aimlessly for a time, and then he drove past the hospital on his way to the parking lot.

—"It's the millionaire banker, Wellington McMillan," said the pretty nurse. "Yes?" said Walter Mitty, removing his gloves slowly. "Who has the case?" "Dr. Renshaw and Dr. Benbow, but there are two specialists here, Dr. Remington from New York and Mr. Pritchard-Mitford from London. He flew over." A door opened down a long, cool corridor and Dr. Renshaw came out. He looked distraught and haggard. "Hello, Mitty," he said. "We're having the devil's own time with McMillan, the millionaire banker and close personal friend of Roosevelt. Obstreosis of the ductal tract. Tertiary. Wish you'd take a look at him." "Glad to," said Mitty.

In the operating room there were whispered introductions: "Dr. Remington, Dr. Mitty, Mr. Pritchard-Mitford, Dr. Mitty." "I've read your book on streptothricosis," said Pritchard-Mitford, shaking hands. "A brilliant performance, sir." "Thank you," said Walter Mitty. "Didn't know you were in the States, Mitty," grumbled Remington. "Coals to Newcastle, bringing Mitford and me up here for a tertiary." "You are very kind," said Mitty. A huge, complicated machine, connected to the operating table, with many tubes and wires, began at this moment to go pocketa-pocketa-pocketa. "The new anaesthetizer is giving way!" shouted an interne. "There is no one in the East who knows how to fix it!" "Quiet, man!" said Mitty, in a low, cool voice. He sprang to the machine, which was now going pocketa-pocketa-queep-pocketa-queep. He began fingering delicately a row of glistening dials. "Give me a fountain pen!" he snapped. Someone handed him a fountain pen.

> Imagination and fiction make up more than three quarters of our real life.
>
> Simone Weil

He pulled a faulty piston out of the machine and inserted the pen in its place. "That will hold for ten minutes," he said. "Get on with the operation." A nurse hurried over and whispered to Renshaw, and Mitty saw the man turn pale. "Coreopsis has set in," said Renshaw nervously. "If you would take over, Mitty?" Mitty looked at him and at the craven figure of Benbow, who drank, and at the grave, uncertain faces of the two great specialists. "If you wish," he said. They slipped a white gown on him; he adjusted a mask and drew on thin gloves; nurses handed him shining—

"Back it up, Mac! Look out for that Buick!" Walter Mitty jammed on the brakes. "Wrong lane, Mac," said the parking-lot attendant, looking at Mitty closely. "Gee. Yeh," muttered Mitty. He began cautiously to back out of the lane marked "Exit Only." "Leave her sit there," said the attendant. "I'll put her away." Mitty got out of the car. "Hey, better leave the key." "Oh," said Mitty, handing the man the ignition key. The attendant vaulted into the car, backed it up with insolent skill, and put it where it belonged.

They're so damn cocky, thought Mitty, walking along Main Street; they think they know everything. Once he had tried to take his chains off, outside New Milford, and he had got them wound around the axles. A man had had to come out in a wrecking car and unwind them, a young, grinning garageman. Since then Mrs. Mitty always made him drive to a garage to have the chains taken off. The next time, he thought, I'll wear my right arm in a sling; they won't grin at me then. I'll have my right arm in a sling and they'll see I couldn't possibly take the chains off myself. He kicked at the slush on the sidewalk. "Overshoes," he said to himself, and he began looking for a shoe store.

When he came out into the street again, with the overshoes in a box under his arm, Walter Mitty began to wonder what the other thing was his wife had told him to get. She had told him twice, before they set out from their house for Waterbury. In a way he hated these weekly trips to town—he was always getting something wrong. Kleenex, he thought, Squibb's, razor blades? No, toothpaste, toothbrush, bicarbonate, carborundum, initiative and referendum? He gave it up. But she would remember it. "Where's the what's-its-name?" she would ask. "Don't tell me you forgot the what's-it's-name." A newsboy went by shouting something about the Waterbury trial.

—"Perhaps this will refresh your memory." The District Attorney suddenly thrust a heavy automatic at the quiet figure on the witness stand. "Have you ever seen this before?" Walter Mitty took the gun and examined it expertly. "This is my Webley-Vickers 50.80," he said calmly. An excited buzz ran around the courtroom. The Judge rapped for order.

"You are a crack shot with any sort of firearms, I believe?" said the District Attorney, insinuatingly. "Objection!" shouted Mitty's attorney. "We have shown that the defendant could not have fired the shot. We have shown that he wore his right arm in a sling on the night of the fourteenth of July." Walter Mitty raised his hand briefly and the bickering attorneys were stilled. "With any known make of gun," he said evenly, "I could have killed Gregory Fitzhurst at three hundred feet *with my left hand*." Pandemonium broke loose in the courtroom. A woman's scream rose above the bedlam and suddenly a lovely, dark-haired girl was in Walter Mitty's arms. The District Attorney struck at her savagely. Without rising from his chair, Mitty let the man have it on the point of the chin. "You miserable cur!"—

"Puppy biscuit," said Walter Mitty. He stopped walking and the buildings of Waterbury rose up out of the misty courtroom and surrounded him again. A woman who was passing laughed. "He said 'Puppy biscuit'," she said to her companion. "That man said 'Puppy biscuit' to himself." Walter Mitty hurried on. He went into an A. & P., not the first one he came to but a smaller one farther up the street. "I want some biscuit for small, young dogs," he said to the clerk. "Any special brand, sir?" The greatest pistol shot in the world thought a moment. "It says 'Puppies Bark for It' on the box," said Walter Mitty.

His wife would be through at the hairdresser's in fifteen minutes, Mitty saw in looking at his watch, unless they had trouble drying it; sometimes they had trouble drying it. She didn't like to get to the hotel first; she would want him to be there waiting for her as usual. He found a big leather chair in the lobby, facing a window, and he put the overshoes and the puppy biscuit on the floor beside it. He picked up an old copy of *Liberty* and sank down in the chair. "Can Germany Conquer the World Through the Air?" Walter Mitty looked at the pictures of bombing planes and of ruined streets.

—"The cannonading has got the wind up in young Raleigh, sir," said the sergeant. Captain Mitty looked up at him through tousled hair. "Get him to bed," he said wearily. "With the others. I'll fly alone." "But you can't, sir," said the sergeant anxiously. "It takes two men to handle that bomber and the Archies are pounding hell out of the air. Von Richtman's circus is between here and Saulier." "Somebody's got to get that ammunition dump," said Mitty. "I'm going over. Spot of brandy?" He poured a drink for the sergeant and one for himself. War thundered and whined around the dugout and battered at the door. There was a rending of wood, and splinters flew through the room. "A bit of a near thing," said Captain Mitty carelessly. "The box barrage is closing in," said the sergeant. "We only live once, Sergeant," said Mitty, with his faint, fleeting smile. "Or do we?" He poured another brandy and tossed it off. "I never see a man could hold his brandy like you, sir," said the sergeant. "Begging your pardon, sir." Captain Mitty stood up and strapped on his huge Webley-Vickers automatic. "It's forty kilometers through hell, sir," said the sergeant. Mitty finished one last brandy. "After all," he said softly, "what isn't?" The pounding of the cannon increased; there was the rat-tat-tatting of machine guns, and from somewhere came the menacing pocketa-pocketa-pocketa of the new flame-throwers. Walter Mitty walked to the door of the dugout humming "Auprès de Ma Blonde." He turned and waved to the sergeant. "Cheerio!" he said.—

Something struck his shoulder. "I've been looking all over this hotel for you," said Mrs. Mitty. "Why do you have to hide in this old chair? How did you expect me to find you?" "Things close in," said Walter Mitty vaguely. "What?" Mrs. Mitty said. "Did you get the what's-its-name? The puppy biscuit? What's in that box?" "Overshoes," said Mitty. "Couldn't you have put them on in the store?" "I was thinking," said Walter Mitty. "Does it ever occur to you that I am sometimes thinking?" She looked at him. "I'm going to take your temperature when I get you home," she said.

They went out through the revolving doors that made a faintly derisive whistling sound when you pushed them. It was two blocks to the parking lot. At the drugstore on the corner she said, "Wait here for me. I forgot something. I won't be a minute." She was more than a minute. Walter Mitty lighted a cigarette. It began to rain, rain with sleet in it. He stood up against the wall of the drugstore, smoking.— He put his shoulders back and his heels together. "To hell with the handkerchief," said Walter Mitty scornfully. He took one last drag on his cigarette and snapped it away. Then, with that faint, fleeting smile playing about his lips, he faced the firing squad; erect and motionless, proud and disdainful, Walter Mitty the Undefeated, inscrutable to the last.

**James Thurber** (1894–1961) was a popular American writer, humorist, and cartoonist. "The Secret Life of Walter Mitty" was published in a collection of stories (1942), and was later adapted as a film (1947). Thurber, after reading the script, is said to have offered ten thousand dollars to *prevent* the film from being made; however, it proved to be very successful at the box office.

1. *Response*
   a. Each of Mitty's five fantasies is initiated by a specific stimulus in the real world. For each daydream, find the stimulus.
   b. Describe Walter Mitty's real life and real character. Contrast this to his secret lives and characters.
   c. Provide at least three good reasons why the author would end the story with a fantasy sequence. Which do you think is the best reason? Why?
   d. Did you find it necessary to look up the uncommon medical and military terms in the story? Explain.

2. *Literature Studies* *Climax and Resolution* Conventional short stories contain a **climax**. In your opinion, does "The Secret Life of Walter Mitty" contain a climax and/or **resolution**? Explain your answer using examples from the story. Speculate on why James Thurber did or did not include these conventional short story elements.

   The **climax** of a story is the high point of the action, where something decisive occurs. The **resolution** follows the climax and traces the final outcome of the central conflict.

3. *Writing* *Short Story* Because Thurber provides us with only Mitty's point of view, the wife does not come across as a sympathetic character. Write a short story in which we are presented with the wife's view of Walter and their relationship. You can either invent a plot sequence or retell parts of Thurber's tale.

4. *Critical Thinking* "The Secret Life of Walter Mitty" contains obvious stereotypes of male and female roles and behaviours. These stereotypes were common in 1942 when the story was written. In a small group, identify and comment on the stereotypes. Do you think the same stereotypes would appear in an updated version of the story? Why or why not? Present your conclusions to the class.

In China, the revolution demanded self-sacrifice, and there were those who put their country before everything else—even love.

# Love Must Not Be Forgotten

## By Zhang Jie

Translated by Gladys Yang

I am thirty, the same age as our People's Republic. For a republic thirty is still young. But a girl of thirty is virtually on the shelf.

Actually, I have a bona fide suitor. Have you seen the Greek sculptor Myron's *Discobolos*? Qiao Lin is the image of that discus thrower. Even the padded clothes he wears in winter fail to hide his fine physique. Bronzed, with clear-cut features, a broad forehead, and large eyes, his appearance alone attracts most girls to him.

But I can't make up my mind to marry him. I'm not clear what attracts me to him, or him to me.

I know people are gossiping behind my back: "Who does she think she is, to be so choosy?"

To them, I'm a nobody playing hard to get. They take offence at such preposterous behaviour.

Of course, I shouldn't be captious. In a society where commercial production still exists, marriage like most other transactions is still a form of barter.

I have known Qiao Lin for nearly two years, yet still cannot fathom whether he keeps so quiet from aversion to talking or from having nothing to say. When, by way of a small intelligence test, I demand his opinion of this or that, he says "good" or "bad" like a child in kindergarten.

Once I asked, "Qiao Lin, why do you love me?" He thought the question over seriously for what seemed an age. I could see from his normally smooth but now wrinkled forehead that the little grey cells in his handsome head were hard at work cogitating. I felt ashamed to have put him on the spot.

Finally he raised his clear childlike eyes to tell me, "Because you're good!"

Loneliness flooded my heart. "Thank you, Qiao Lin!" I couldn't help wondering, if we were to marry, whether we could discharge our duties to each other as husband and wife. Maybe, because law and morality would have bound us together. But how tragic simply to comply with law and morality! Was there no stronger bond to link us?

When such thoughts cross my mind I have the strange sensation that instead of being a girl contemplating marriage I am an elderly social scientist.

Perhaps I worry too much. We can live like most married couples, bringing up children together, strictly true to each other according to the law.... Although living in the seventies of the twentieth century, people still consider marriage the way they did millennia ago, as a means of continuing the race, a form of barter, or a business transaction in which love and marriage can be separated. As this is the common practice, why shouldn't we follow suit?

But I still can't make up my mind. As a child, I remember, I often cried all night for no rhyme or reason, unable to sleep and disturbing the whole household. My old nurse, a shrewd though uneducated woman, said an ill wind had blown through my ear. I think this judgement showed prescience, because I still have that old weakness. I upset myself over things which really present no problem, upsetting other people at the same time. One's nature is hard to change.

I think of my mother too. If she were alive, what would she say about my attitude to Qiao Lin and my uncertainty about marrying him?

My thoughts constantly turn to her, not because she was such a strict mother that her ghost is still watching over me since her death. No, she was not just my mother but my closest friend. I loved her so much that the thought of her leaving me makes my heart ache.

She never lectured me, just told me quietly in her deep, unwomanly voice about her successes and failures, so that I could learn from her experience. She had evidently not had many successes—her life was full of failures.

During her last days she followed me with her fine, expressive eyes, as if wondering how I would manage on my own and as if she had some important advice for me but hesitated to give it. She must have been worried by my naiveté and sloppy ways. She suddenly blurted out, "Shanshan, if you aren't sure what you want, don't rush into marriage—better live on your own!"

Other people might think this strange advice from a mother to her daughter, but to me it embodied her bitter experience. I don't think she underestimated me or my knowledge of life. She loved me and didn't want me to be unhappy.

"I don't want to marry, mum!" I said, not out of bashfulness or a show of coyness. I can't think why a girl should pretend to be coy. She had long since taught me about things not generally mentioned to girls.

"If you meet the right man, then marry him. Only if he's right for you!"

"I'm afraid no such man exists!"

"That's not true. But it's hard. The world is so vast, I'm afraid you may never meet him." Whether I married or not was not what concerned her, but the quality of the marriage.

"Haven't you managed fine without a husband?"

"Who says so?"

"I think you've done fine."

"I had no choice...." She broke off, lost in thought, her face wistful. Her wistful lined face reminded me of a withered flower I had pressed in a book.

"Why did you have no choice?"

"You ask too many questions," she parried, not ashamed to confide in me but afraid that I might reach the wrong conclusion. Besides, everyone treasures a secret to carry to the grave. Feeling a bit put out, I demanded bluntly, "Didn't you love my dad?"

"No, I never loved him."

"Did he love you?"

"No, he didn't."

"Then why get married?"

She paused, searching for the right words to explain this mystery, then answered bitterly, "When you're young you don't always know what you're looking for, what you need, and people may talk you into getting married. As you grow older and more experienced you find out your true needs. By then, though, you've done many foolish things for which you could kick yourself. You'd give anything to be able to make a fresh start and live more wisely. Those content with their lot will always be happy, they say, but I shall never enjoy that happiness." She added self-mockingly, "A wretched idealist, that's all I am."

Did I take after her? Did we both have genes which attracted ill winds?

"Why don't you marry again?"

"I'm afraid I'm still not sure what I really want." She was obviously unwilling to tell me the truth.

I cannot remember my father. He and Mother split up when I was very small. I just recall her telling me sheepishly that he was a fine handsome fellow. I could see she was ashamed of having judged by appearances and made a futile choice. She told me, "When I can't sleep at night, I force myself to sober up by recalling all those stupid blunders I made. Of course it's so distasteful that I often hide my face in the sheet for shame, as if there were eyes watching me in the dark. But distasteful as it is, I take some pleasure in this form of atonement."

I was really sorry that she hadn't remarried. She was such a fascinating character, if she'd married a man she loved, what a happy household ours would surely have been. Though not beautiful, she had the simple charm of an ink landscape. She was a fine writer too. Another author who knew her well used to say teasingly, "Just reading your works is enough to make anyone love you!"

She would retort, "If he knew that the object of his affection was a white-haired old crone, that would frighten him away."

At her age, she must have known what she really wanted, so this was obviously an evasion. I say this because she had quirks which puzzled me.

For instance, whenever she left Beijing on a trip, she always took with her one of the twenty-seven volumes of Chekhov's stories published between 1950 and 1955. She also warned me, "Don't touch these books. If you want to read Chekhov, read that set I bought you." There was no need to caution me. Having a set of my own why should I touch hers? Besides, she'd told me this over and over again. Still she was on her guard. She seemed bewitched by those books.

So we had two sets of Chekhov's stories at home. Not just because we loved Chekhov, but to parry other people like me who loved Chekhov. Whenever anyone asked to borrow a volume, she would lend one of mine. Once, in her absence, a close friend took a volume from her set. When she found out she was frantic, and at once took a volume of mine to exchange for it.

Ever since I can remember, those books were on her bookcase. Although I admire Chekhov as a great writer, I was puzzled by the way she never tired of reading him. Why, for over twenty years, had she had to read him every single day?

Sometimes, when tired of writing, she poured herself a cup of strong tea and sat down in front of the bookcase, staring raptly at that set of books. If I went into her room then it flustered her, and she either spilt her tea or blushed like a girl discovered with her lover.

I wondered: Has she fallen in love with Chekhov? She might have if he'd still been alive.

When her mind was wandering just before her death, her last words to me were: "That set...." She hadn't the strength to give it its complete title. But I knew what she meant. "And my diary ... 'Love Must Not Be Forgotten' .... Cremate them with me."

I carried out her last instruction regarding the works of Chekhov, but couldn't bring myself to destroy her diary. I thought, if it could be published, it would surely prove the most moving thing she had written. But naturally publication was out of the question.

At first I imagined the entries were raw material she had jotted down. They read neither like stories, essays, a diary, or letters. But after reading the whole I formed a hazy impression, helped out by my imperfect memory. Thinking it over, I finally realized that this was no lifeless manuscript I was holding, but an anguished, loving heart. For over twenty years one man had occupied her heart, but he was not for her. She used these diaries as a substitute for him, a means of pouring out her feelings to him, day after day, year after year.

No wonder she had never considered any eligible proposals, had turned a deaf ear to idle talk whether well-meant or malicious. Her heart was already full, to the exclusion of anybody else. "No lake can compare with the ocean, no cloud with those on Mount Wu." Remembering those lines I often reflected sadly that few people in real life could love like this. No one would love me like this.

I learned that towards the end of the thirties, when this man was doing underground work for the Party in Shanghai, an old worker had given his life to cover him, leaving behind a helpless wife and daughter. Out of a sense of duty, of gratitude to the dead and deep class feeling, he had unhesitatingly married the girl. When he saw the endless troubles caused by "love" of couples who had married for "love," he may have thought, "Thank Heaven, though I didn't marry for love, we get on well, able to help each other." For years, as man and wife they lived through hard times.

He must have been my mother's colleague. Had I ever met him? He couldn't have visited our home. Who was he?

In the spring of 1962, Mother took me to a concert. We went on foot, the theatre being quite near.

A black limousine pulled up silently by the pavement. Out stepped an elderly man with white hair in a black serge tunic-suit. What a striking shock of white hair! Strict, scrupulous, distinguished, transparently honest—that was my impression of him. The cold glint of his flashing eyes reminded me of lightning or swordplay. Only ardent love for a woman really deserving his love could fill cold eyes like those with tenderness.

He walked up to Mother and said, "How are you, Comrade Zhong Yu? It's been a long time."

"How are you!" Mother's hand holding mine suddenly turned icy cold and trembled a little.

They stood face to face without looking at each other, each appearing upset, even stern. Mother fixed her eyes on the trees by the roadside, not yet in leaf. He looked at me. "Such a big girl already. Good, fine—you take after your mother."

Instead of shaking hands with Mother he shook hands with me. His hand was as icy as hers and trembling a little. As if transmitting an electric current, I felt a sudden shock. Snatching my hand away I cried, "There's nothing good about that!"

"Why not?" he asked with a surprised expression grown-ups always have when children speak out frankly.

I glanced at Mother's face. I did take after her, to my disappointment. "Because she's not beautiful!"

This is one of a series of post-cards produced in China during the Cultural Revolution. How does this artist use colour to create mood? What messages, explicit or implicit, are sent by this postcard?

Untitled postcard by an unknown artist

He laughed, then said teasingly, "Too bad that there should be a child who doesn't find her own mother beautiful. Do you remember in '53, when your mum was transferred to Beijing, she came to our ministry to report for duty? She left you outside on the verandah, but like a monkey you climbed all the stairs, peeped through the cracks in doors, and caught your finger in the door of my office. You sobbed so bitterly that I carried you off to find her."

"I don't remember that." I was annoyed at his harking back to a time when I was still in open-seat pants.

"Ah, we old people have better memories." He turned abruptly and remarked to Mother, "I've read that last story of yours. Frankly speaking, there's something not quite right about it. You shouldn't have condemned the heroine.... There's nothing wrong with falling in love, as long as you don't spoil someone else's life.... In fact, the hero might have loved her too. Only for the sake of a third person's happiness, they had to renounce their love...."

A policeman came over to where the car was parked and ordered the driver to move on. When the driver made some excuse, the old man looked round. After a hasty "Goodbye" he strode to the car and told the policeman, "Sorry. It's not his fault, it's mine...."

I found it amusing watching this old cadre listening respectfully to the policeman's strictures. When I turned to Mother with a mischievous smile, she looked as upset as a first-form primary schoolchild standing forlornly in front of the stern headmistress. Anyone would have thought she was the one being lectured by the policeman.

The car drove off, leaving a puff of smoke. Very soon even this smoke vanished with the wind, as if nothing at all had happened. But the incident stuck in my mind.

Analyzing it now, he must have been the man whose strength of character won Mother's heart. That strength came from his firm political convictions, his narrow escapes from death in the Revolution, his active brain, his drive at work, his well-cultivated mind. Besides, strange to say, he and Mother both liked the oboe. Yes, she must have worshipped him. She once told me that unless she worshipped a man, she couldn't love him even for one day.

But I could not tell whether he loved her or not. If not, why was there this entry in her diary?

"This is far too fine a present. But how did you know that Chekhov's my favourite writer?"

"You said so."

"I don't remember that."

"I remember. I heard you mention it when you were chatting with someone."

So he was the one who had given her the *Selected Stories of Chekhov*. For her that was tantamount to a love letter.

Maybe this man, who didn't believe in love, realized by the time his hair was white that in his heart was something which could be called love. By the time he no longer had the right to love, he made the tragic discovery of this love for which he would have given his life. Or did it go deeper than that?

This is all I remember about him.

How wretched Mother must have been, deprived of the man to whom she was devoted! To catch a glimpse of his car or the back of his head through its rear window, she carefully figured out which roads he would take to work and back. Whenever he made a speech, she sat at the back of the hall watching his face rendered hazy by cigarette smoke and poor lighting. Her eyes would brim with tears, but she swallowed them back. If a fit of coughing made him break off, she wondered anxiously why no one persuaded him to give up smoking. She was afraid he would get bronchitis again. Why was he so near yet so far?

He, to catch a glimpse of her, looked out of the car window every day, straining his eyes to watch the streams of cyclists, afraid that she might have an accident. On the rare evenings on which he had no meetings, he would walk by a roundabout way to our neighbourhood, to pass our compound gate. However busy, he would always make time to look in papers and journals for her work.

His duty had always been clear to him, even in the most difficult times. But now confronted by this love he became a weakling, quite helpless. At his age it was laughable. Why should life play this trick on him?

Yet when they happened to meet at work, each tried to avoid the other, hurrying off with a nod. Even so, this would make Mother blind and deaf to everything around her. If she met a colleague named Wang she would call him Guo and mutter something unintelligible.

It was a cruel ordeal for her. She wrote:

> We agreed to forget each other. But I deceived you, I have never forgotten. I don't think you've forgotten either. We're just deceiving each other, hiding our misery. I haven't deceived you deliberately, though; I did my best to carry out our agreement. I often stay far away from Beijing, hoping time and distance will help me to forget you. But on my

return, as the train pulls into the station, my head reels. I stand on the platform looking round intently, as if someone were waiting for me. Of course there is no one. I realize then that I have forgotten nothing. Everything is unchanged. My love is like a tree the roots of which strike deeper year after year—I have no way to uproot it.

At the end of every day, I feel as if I've forgotten something important. I may wake with a start from my dreams wondering what has happened. But nothing has happened. Nothing. Then it comes home to me that you are missing! So everything seems lacking, incomplete, and there is nothing to fill up the blank. We are nearing the ends of our lives, why should we be carried away by emotion like children? Why should life submit people to such ordeals, then unfold before you your lifelong dream? Because I started off blindly I took the wrong turning, and now there are insuperable obstacles between me and my dream.

Yes, Mother never let me go to the station to meet her when she came back from a trip, preferring to stand alone on the platform and imagine that he had met her. Poor mother with her greying hair was as infatuated as a girl.

Not much space in the diary was devoted to their romance. Most entries dealt with trivia: Why one of her articles had not come off; her fear that she had no real talent; the excellent play she missed by mistaking the time on the ticket; the drenching she got by going out for a stroll without her umbrella. In spirit they were together day and night, like a devoted married couple. In fact, they spent no more than twenty-four hours together in all. Yet in that time they experienced deeper happiness than some people in a whole lifetime. Shakespeare makes Juliet say, "I cannot sum up half my sum of wealth." And probably that is how Mother felt.

He must have been killed in the Cultural Revolution. Perhaps because of the conditions then, that section of the diary is ambiguous and obscure. Mother had been so fiercely attacked for her writing, it amazed me that she went on keeping a diary. From some veiled allusions I gathered that he had queried the theories advanced by that "theoretician" then at the height of favour, and had told someone, "This is sheer Rightist talk." It was clear from the tear-stained pages of Mother's diary that he had been harshly denounced; but the steadfast old man never knuckled under to the authorities. His last words were, "When I go to meet Marx, I shall go on fighting my case!"

That must have been in the winter of 1969, because that was when Mother's hair turned white overnight, though she was not yet fifty. And she put on a black arm-band. Her position then was extremely difficult. She was criticized for wearing this old-style mourning, and ordered to say for whom she was in mourning.

"For whom are you wearing that, mum?" I asked anxiously.

"For my lover." Not to frighten me she explained, "Someone you never knew."

"Shall I put one on too?" She patted my cheeks, as she had when I was a child. It was years since she had shown me such affection. I often felt that as she aged, especially during these last years of persecution, all tenderness had left her, or was concealed in her heart, so that she seemed like a man.

She smiled sadly and said, "No, you needn't wear one."

Her eyes were as dry as if she had no more tears to shed. I longed to comfort her or do something to please her. But she said, "Off you go."

I felt an inexplicable dread, as if dear Mother had already half left me. I blurted out, "Mum!"

Quick to sense my desolation, she said gently, "Don't be afraid. Off you go. Leave me alone for a little." I was right. She wrote:

> You have gone. Half my soul seems to have taken flight with you. I had no means of knowing what had become of you, much less of seeing you for the last time. I had no right to ask either, not being your wife or friend.... So we are torn apart. If only I could have borne that inhuman treatment for you, so that you could have lived on! You should have lived to see your name cleared and take up your work again, for the sake of those who loved you. I knew you could not be a counter-revolutionary. You were one of the finest men killed. That's why I love you—I am not afraid now to avow it.
>
> Snow is whirling down. Heavens, even God is such a hypocrite, he is using this whiteness to cover up your blood and the scandal of your murder.
>
> I have never set store by my life. But now I keep wondering whether anything I say or do would make you contract your shaggy eyebrows in a frown. I must live a worthwhile life like you, and do some honest work for our country. Things can't go on like this—those criminals will get what's coming to them.
>
> I used to walk alone along that small asphalt road, the only

place where we once walked together, hearing my footsteps in the silent night.... I always paced to and fro and lingered there, but never as wretchedly as now. Then, though you were not beside me, I knew you were still in this world and felt that you were keeping me company. Now I can hardly believe that you have gone.

At the end of the road I would retrace my steps, then walk along it again.

Rounding the fence I always looked back, as if you were still standing there waving goodbye. We smiled faintly, like casual acquaintances, to conceal our undying love. That ordinary evening in early spring, a chilly wind was blowing as we walked silently away from each other. You were wheezing a little because of your chronic bronchitis. That upset me. I wanted to beg you to slow down, but somehow I couldn't. We both walked very fast, as if some important business were waiting for us. How we prized that single stroll we had together, but we were afraid we might lose control of ourselves and burst out with "I love you"—those three words which had tormented us for years. Probably no one else could believe that we never once even clasped hands!

No, Mother, I believe it. I am the only one able to see into your locked heart.

Ah, that little asphalt road, so haunted by bitter memories. We shouldn't overlook the most insignificant spots on earth. For who knows how much secret grief and joy they may hide.

No wonder that when tired of writing, she would pace slowly along that little road behind our window. Sometimes at dawn after a sleepless night, sometimes on a moonless, windy evening. Even in winter during howling gales which hurled sand and pebbles against the window pane.... I thought this was one of her eccentricities, not knowing that she had gone to meet him in spirit.

She liked to stand by the window too, staring at the small asphalt road. Once I thought from her expression that one of our closest friends must be coming to call. I hurried to the window. It was a late autumn evening. The cold wind was stripping dead leaves from the trees and blowing them down the small empty road.

She went on pouring out her heart to him in her diary as she had when he was alive. Right up to the day when the pen slipped from her fingers. Her last message was:

I am a materialist, yet I wish there were a Heaven. For then, I know, I would find you there waiting for me. I am going there to join you, to be together for eternity. We need never be parted again or keep at a distance for fear of spoiling someone else's life. Wait for me, dearest, I am coming—

I do not know how Mother, on her deathbed, could still love so ardently with all her heart. To me it seemed not love but a form of madness, a passion stronger than death. If undying love really exists, she reached its extreme. She obviously died happy, because she had known true love. She had no regrets.

Now these old people's ashes have mingled with the elements. But I know that, no matter what form they may take, they still love each other. Though not bound together by earthly laws or morality, though they never once clasped hands, each possessed the other completely. Nothing could part them. Centuries to come, if one white cloud trails another, two grasses grow side by side, one wave splashes another, a breeze follows another ... believe me, that will be them.

Each time I read that diary "Love Must Not Be Forgotten" I cannot hold back my tears. I often weep bitterly, as if I myself experienced their ill-fated love. If not a tragedy it was too laughable. No matter how beautiful or moving I find it, I have no wish to follow suit!

Thomas Hardy wrote that "the call seldom produces the comer, the man to love rarely coincides with the hour for loving." I cannot censure them from conventional moral standards. What I deplore is that they did not wait for a "missing counterpart" to call them.

If everyone could wait, instead of rushing into marriage, how many tragedies could be averted!

When we reach communism, will there still be cases of marriage without love? Maybe, because since the world is so vast, two kindred spirits may be unable to answer each other's call. But how tragic! However, by that time, there may be ways to escape such tragedies.

Why should I split hairs?

Perhaps after all we are responsible for these tragedies. Who knows? Maybe we should take the responsibility for the old ideas handed down from the past. Because if someone never marries, that is a challenge to these ideas. You will be called neurotic, accused of having guilty secrets or having made political mistakes. You may be regarded as an eccentric who looks down on ordinary people, not respecting age-old customs—a heretic. In short they will trump up endless vulgar and futile charges to ruin your reputation. Then you have to knuckle under to those ideas and marry willy-nilly. But once you put the chains of a loveless marriage around your neck, you will suffer for it for the rest of your life.

I long to shout: "Mind your own business! Let us wait patiently for our counterparts. Even waiting in vain is better than willy-nilly marriage. To live single is not such a fearful disaster. I believe it may be a sign of a step forward in culture, education, and the quality of life."

**Zhang Jie** was born in 1937 in Beijing, China. She studied economics, but turned to writing, beginning with scripts for the Beijing Film Studio. She has written many short stories since the end of the Cultural Revolution in 1976, and these have established her as a popular and controversial writer.

1. *Response*
   a. Were you able to make personal connections to the characters and situations in the story? Explain your response.
   b. Describe some of the different ways in which the mother nurtures her love for the nameless man. Do you think her devotion is admirable or foolish? Explain.
   c. Why do you think the author, Zhang Jie, chose to narrate the story from the daughter's point of view?

2. *Research and Inquiry* Compile some background information that would help a reader better appreciate the historical and cultural context of "Love Must Not Be Forgotten." First, look through the story for dates, places, and key terms that you can use to guide your research. Summarize your findings in a page or less of background information.

3. *Language Conventions* Personal Pronouns Read the mother's speech on page 41 ("She paused, searching for the right words ..."). Note the shift in the personal pronouns she uses in this paragraph. What does the shift reveal about her character?

4. *Critical Thinking* What social message does the author, Zhang Jie, convey in her story? Do you think the message is relevant to contemporary Canadians? Present your answer in a brief opinion piece. State your viewpoint clearly and articulate the reasons for your position.

# Saturday Climbing

## By W.D. Valgardson

*"Gradually, as a dozen Saturdays passed, what had seemed impossible was reduced to the merely difficult."*

Sixty feet up the cliff, the toe of his climbing boot resting on a ledge no wider than a dime, two fingers curled around a nubbin of rock, Barry was suddenly afraid that he would fall.

"Rope," he called.

At the foot of the cliff, his daughter let out the golden line of rope that joined them.

As Barry felt the rope go slack, he raised his right knee and pressed his toe into a shallow depression. Grunting with the strain, he stood up on his right leg, then paused, uncertain of his next move.

The cliff had proven to be deceptive. The conglomerate, with its rough, gravel-like surface, had looked easy. Close to the base, there were large handholds, so that at first the climbing was little more difficult than walking up stairs. Then, unexpectedly, the surfaces smoothed; the places where he could get a secure hold were spread farther and farther apart. At the same time, the numerous cracks dwindled until there was no place to set any protection. Unable to go back because of his pride, he had continued on until he now found himself dangerously far above his last piton. If he fell, he would drop twenty-five feet to the piton, then twenty-five feet past it before his rope came taut and held him. There was, because of the elasticity of the rope, a chance that he would ground out.

The thought flitted through his mind that it would be like falling from the top of a six-storey building. Tensing his fingers, he straightened his elbow and leaned back from the rock so that he could search for his next hold. Above him, there was a half-inch ledge. He reached up, got a good grip, then lifted his left leg higher than he had ever imagined he could and set his foot on a rough patch that would provide the necessary friction to hold his weight.

He had been scared many times but never like this. Never before had he been this close to paralysis, to a sensation of letting go so that the tension and the fear would be over. The way he felt, he imagined, was the way a wounded animal felt when it finally gave up fleeing and allowed itself to be killed.

Six inches from his left hand there was a vertical crack that seemed hardly wider than a fingernail. Cautiously, he explored it with his fingers. Just within his reach it widened slightly. He ran his hand over his rack and unsnapped the smallest chock nut. He forced the aluminum wedge deep into the crack. From the wedge there hung a wire loop and from that a carabiner. Catching hold of the rope tied to his harness, he lifted it up, forced open the spring-loaded gate of the carabiner and fitted the rope into the aluminum oval.

Once the gate snapped shut, he sighed with relief. The chock nut, the wire loop, the carabiner, the rope, fragile as they looked, would hold ten times his weight. If he wanted to, he could let go and simply hang in space.

"You all right?" his daughter called. "Yeah," he lied. "Just resting."

His voice sounded faint and breathy. He was glad she could not see his momentary weakness. He could not control the trembling of his legs. The muscle of his right arm jerked spasmodically. Ever since his wife had left him, he had tried to compensate by providing unhesitating leadership for his daughter. He did his best to keep life simple and uncomplicated. It was, he thought, the way to provide security.

He glanced down. Among the scattered grey boulders, Moira's red hair gleamed like a burnished cap.

"You're doing fine," she hollered. The crosscurrents of air that played over the cliff face blurred her voice, making it seem farther away than it really was. To hear what she said, he had to strain toward the sound. "You've got another twenty feet to a big ledge. You can do it easy."

He was grateful for her confidence. Before they had started climbing, there had crept into his daughter's voice a constant note of disparagement and disappointment. The times he had managed to overcome his own insecurity and had asked her what was the matter, she had turned her back on him, answering, "Nothing," with a tightly controlled voice.

Bewildered, he had sought the advice of women at work who had teenage daughters. They had been no help. Behind their competent, efficient professional selves, they too, he realized, were just as confused as he was. In desperation, he had gone so far as to pose the question of the relationship of fathers and daughters to his class. He had not been prepared for the reaction he got. From every corner of the room came cries of bitter disappointment and resentment.

As he had left the classroom, one student had called to him. He had stopped to wait for her. She had frizzy dark hair, wore long dresses that might have come from a western movie set, a rainbow assortment of beads, and a nose ring. She always talked as if she was thinking in some exotic language and was translating it badly. She was the only student he'd ever had who insisted on analysing *War and Peace*[1] by consulting the *I Ching*.[2]

"The caged bird proves nothing but the power of the captor," she had intoned.

For a moment, he suffered vertigo, and the cliff seemed to sway as if in an earthquake. He pressed his forehead to the cool stone and shut his eyes. Inside his flesh, his bones trembled.

Taking up rock-climbing had been an act of desperation. All the past activities Moira and he had done together—going to foreign films, visiting Seattle, beachcombing—she dismissed with a contemptuous shrug of her shoulders. At one time, they had played chess nearly every day. Lately, she pretended she had never seen the game. When he had noticed an advertisement for rock-climbing, he remembered that she had spoken admiringly of classmates who had hiked the West Coast Trail. He had registered them and paid their fees. Then he informed her.

He hoped she would be pleased. Instead, she was incensed that he had committed her to something without her consent. He knew she was right to be angry but he was too frantic to care. Over the previous month, she had come home late a number of times. Each time, the sweet-sour smell of marijuana clung to her, and her pupils seemed unnaturally large. He had not dared to accuse her of smoking dope. If he was wrong, she would never forgive him for being unjust. Being right frightened him even more. If she said, "That's right, I'm smoking dope, six joints a day, and sniffing coke and participating in orgies," he didn't know what he would do. Ranting and raving had ceased to work. Reasoning with her had no effect. He felt utterly helpless.

By emphasizing that the money was spent and there was no refund, he won the argument over rock-climbing. However, he took the car to the first class while she took her bike. She went prepared to sneer at everything, but once she saw her classmates, her attitude changed. Instead of Moira being isolated by her youth, Barry was isolated because of his age. Of the fifteen members, eleven were under twenty. The instructor still didn't need to shave more than once a week.

By the time the three hours were over and he realized that rock-

---

[1] *War and Peace:* novel by the Russian author Leo Tolstoy
[2] *I Ching:* ancient Chinese book used to foretell the future

climbing wasn't going to be rough hiking, it was too late to back out. There were only three girls in the class. In return for the attention of one-third of the young men, Moira was prepared to scale the Himalayas.

Barry began with an attitude that was typical of someone raised on the Prairies. Anything over three feet was a substantial elevation. During the second class, he was expected to climb vertical cliffs. He gave some thought to dropping out of the class but realized that, after the fuss he had made about the fees, he would look like a dreadful hypocrite.

Gradually, as a dozen Saturdays passed, what had seemed impossible was reduced to the merely difficult. Cliffs that had looked flat and smooth as polished marble became a series of problems and solutions. The names of the unfamiliar equipment became a part of his vocabulary. Young men in climbing boots frequented his backyard and kitchen. To his relief, Moira accepted him enough to spend an occasional hour practising knot-tying with him.

This weekend there had been no class. In an attempt to heal a rift caused by an argument over her going away to college—she was two years ahead of herself in school and, therefore, in spite of being in grade 12 was only 16—he had offered to go climbing with her. To his surprise, she'd accepted.

"Climbing," he called.

"Climb on," Moira answered.

He stepped up, away from the safety of his perch. His life, he realized, was in her hands. If he fell, she was his protection.

The thought of giving her so much responsibility was like the prick of a thorn. In all other things, he had been trying to keep her from rushing headlong into taking on too much responsibility at once. The result had been a long series of disagreements. She did not have the decency to let one dispute finish before she began another. Sometimes three or four overlapped.

On Fridays, when he went to the faculty club, he ordered double brandies and brooded over whether he shouldn't have insisted on Sunday school in a good fundamentalist church all the past years. His colleagues, the majority of whom were the epitome of liberal tolerance about most things, when they talked about their teenage children reverted to wistful fantasies about convents and boarding schools in inaccessible locations.

The weekend past, Moira had wanted to go to an all-night party with a boy he just vaguely recognized as having drifted through the house two or three times. Barry was dumbfounded. At the same age, he'd had to have his girlfriends in before midnight. If he had kept a girl out all night, her father would have met them with a shotgun.

"Good girls," he said, quoting something he'd heard in adolescence, "don't stay out all night."

"Good fathers," she shot back, "don't think the worst of their daughters."

That afternoon was filled with slamming doors, weeping and raised voices. He found himself fighting so hard against her staying out all night that he compromised on three o'clock and afterward, when he had calmed down, wondered how it had happened. He had been determined to start with a deadline of midnight and let himself be persuaded to accept one o'clock. Although Moira claimed not to remember the chess moves, he had the distinct feeling that he'd been checkmated.

The final blow had been her insistence on going away to college. They had the money, he admitted. It just wasn't sensible, at sixteen, to travel 2,000 miles to attend a school when the local university was every bit as good, even if it did have him on the faculty. He suspected the choice had more to do with her all-night-party boy than with academic excellence.

Now, as he worked his way up toward the large ledge where he was to set up a belay station, it was as if Barry were in danger of being pulled backward by the sheer weight of his memories. It was with a sense of relief that he heaved himself onto the ledge. He paused to catch his breath, then anchored himself to a boulder.

"On belay," he shouted down, giving Moira the signal that he was ready.

His daughter, eighty feet below, seemed so small that Barry felt he could lift her into his arms. She looked no larger than she had been when, at three, she had eaten a bottle of aspirin. He had scooped her up and run with her four blocks to the hospital. After that desperate race and the struggle to hold her down—it had taken both him and a nurse to control her flailing limbs while the doctor had pumped her stomach—he was acutely aware of how tenuous her life was, of how much he would suffer if he lost her. For a long time afterward, he thought of her as being intricately constructed of fragile paper.

"Climbing," Moira answered.

"Climb on," he shouted.

From time to time, she paused to pull loose the chock nuts and

> People create stories create people; or rather
> stories create people create stories.
>
> Chinua Achebe

pitons her father had left behind. These, since they would be needed later, she clipped to a sling that hung over her shoulder. Once, when she deviated from the route her father had taken, she became stuck at an overhang. Not having dealt with the obstacle himself, Barry could not help and had to leave her to find her own solution.

The climb seemed agonizingly slow, as if it would never be completed. Then, when it was over, and his daughter, grinning, breathless, was climbing over the edge, it was as if hardly any time had passed.

They sat side by side, sipping orange juice, their feet dangling in space.

"I thought you were in trouble," Moira said.

"I thought you were too," he replied, matching his weakness with hers. Then, ashamed, he admitted, "I gripped."

Moira twisted about. Her red hair was snugged at the back with a rubber band. Being outside had sprinkled her nose with light freckles.

She studied the cliff face. It rose another hundred feet. There was a crack that ran more than halfway, then a small series of outcrops. He tried to see the route they should take, but the last ten or fifteen feet seemed impossible.

"I'd come home for Christmas," she said in a rush, "and classes are out in April. It's not as if it was such a long time to be away."

She had caught him unawares, and none of his carefully prepared arguments were at hand.

"It's just so unexpected," was all that he could manage.

"I've got to leave sometime."

The house will be so empty, he wanted to say. How will I get used to being alone? It is as if you lost your first tooth only last year. As if I took you to kindergarten six months ago. You're barely rid of your braces.

She lifted her index finger and rubbed the side of her nose. She had done it as long as he could remember. It was her signal that she was going to impart a confidence or confess a wrongdoing—that she liked some boy in her class, that she had got a detention or spent all her allowance before the end of the week and needed more money.

"I'm not innocent, you know."

He wondered what she meant by that but was afraid to ask.

"I mean," she continued, "Vic Hi's a big school. You hear a lot. Everybody's on the Pill. The dope's there if you want it. There's lots of opportunity."

He was tempted to let loose his anxiety in a lecture, but the memory of the frizzy-haired student in his class stopped him. She had stood on one foot all the time they were talking, the sole of her left sandal pressed to her right knee. She had passed her hand before his face in an affected arc. He'd heard her father was a prominent lawyer in the East but found it hard to believe.

She had talked in aphorisms and riddles, then a silence had fallen between them. He'd wondered why she had bothered to call after him, what she had really wanted to say. He had left her but, after a few steps, glanced back. She had given up her storklike stance and was standing with feet together, shoulders slumped, her face slack beneath her gaudy makeup. For the first time, he had seen how much younger she was than he had thought. If he had not known better, he'd have said she was a lost child.

Just then, she had seen him watching her. Immediately, she had drawn up her shoulders, flung back her head, given an exaggerated sway of her hips and pranced away. That had been the last time he'd seen her. She had never come back to his class, and one day a yellow drop-slip with her name on it had appeared in his mailbox.

"I want to lead this pitch," Moira said.

Barry was startled. She had never led. Always before she'd been second or third on a rope.

"I was thinking of rappelling down," he answered. "I can't see a clear route up."

"There," she said. "There and there and there." She jabbed her fingertip at a series of holds.

"But where would you set your protection?"

Her hand wove a series of stitches in the air. "There. Up there. To the side. Back across. Up about six feet."

His fear for her was not without reason. The climbing, after seeming so dangerous at first, had begun to lose its aura of hazard. They all fell from time to time, but their ropes kept them from suffering more than bruised knees and elbows. Then, one of the climbers who was leading had ignored instructions and, overconfident, had put in only one piece of protection. He placed it improperly, and when he slipped and fell, his weight jerked it loose. For a moment, no one had been able to move, then those who were not belaying or climbing had run toward the boy who lay sprawled on his back. Bright red blood seeped from his nose and ear.

"Jackets," Barry had demanded. Red Cross training that he'd not thought about in years came back with an intense clarity. "Every piece of clothing you can spare. We mustn't let him get cold."

They all had moved automatically, clumsily, unable to think. Having done as he instructed, they all stood stupefied. Their faces were shocked white beneath their tans.

He sent two of the students racing down the hill for help.

For an hour, they huddled in a ragged circle around the boy whose hair was paler than the sun-drenched grass and whose skin might have been moulded from wax. He slipped in and out of consciousness. Each time his eyes shut, they all tensed, afraid that he had died. But then, he would groan or let out his breath harshly, and the moment would pass. Someone, Barry had not noticed who, had started collecting gear. One, and then another, began to pack. They moved slowly, silently, as if any noise would disturb the delicate balance between life and death.

*Grounded out.* That was what they called it. Because his safety had not been properly set, he had grounded out. Barry remembered that the air force had been like that too. Pilots never failed. They washed out. They never died. They bought it. *Grounded out.* The semantics covered up the fear.

Now, for a moment, it was as if, once again, he could hear the sharp startled cry; see the backward arc, the body, falling without grace or beauty, the rope writhing and twisting, the red-shirted boy settling in a cloud of unexpected dust.

"Ron," Barry protested, surprising himself at remembering the boy's name.

"Do you think I'd be so careless?"

It was asked in a tone that allowed no argument.

Stiffly, he stood up and tested his belay.

*Don't climb*, he thought, *it's too dangerous. Let us go back the way we came and find somewhere that'll always be safe.* But even as he thought it, he knew that it was impossible.

Once again, it was as if he were standing before the frizzy-haired girl, watching her long green nails sweep slowly before his face. At the time, he had not wanted to understand. "The world seeks balance," she'd said. "Extremism begets extremism."

"On belay," he said.

"Climbing," Moira replied.

His daughter, easily, with the supreme confidence of youth, grasped a handhold and pulled herself onto a flake. Smoothly, she worked her way up one side of the crack, straddled it and crossed over.

Below her, her father, ever watchful, full of fear, smoothly payed out the rope, determined to give her all the slack she needed while, at the same time, keeping his hands tensed, ready to lock shut, ready to absorb the shock of any fall. ❿

**W.D. Valgardson** was born in 1939 and grew up in Gimli, Manitoba. He now lives in British Columbia. He is a poet, novelist, short story writer, and playwright, and teaches writing at the University of Victoria. For "Saturday Climbing," Valgardson drew on personal experience—his hobbies include rock climbing and hiking.

1. *Response*
   **a.** The protagonist of a story is the main character. Who do you think is the protagonist of "Saturday Climbing"? Explain.
   **b.** "Saturday Climbing" tells the story of a parent-teenager relationship from the perspective of the parent. As a teenager, what is your reaction? Do you think W.D. Valgardson does a good job of capturing some of the challenges that parents and teenagers face? Is Moira's perspective fairly represented? Give reasons for your opinions.
   **c.** What does the ending of the story suggest about the changes that are occurring in the relationship between the father and daughter? Use specific details to support your answer.

2. *Literature Studies* Plot A short story often contains more than one plot. In a small group, identify the different plots in "Saturday Climbing" and show the parallels among them. Why do you think the author chose to tell this story using multiple plots?

3. *Media* Poster In "Saturday Climbing," Valgardson uses setting in a symbolic way; rock climbing becomes a metaphor for a parent–teenager relationship. Create a poster that also uses rock climbing imagery to express one of the themes or messages in the story. The image(s) you select for your poster should complement the title, caption, and/or text you use to convey the message.

*Folk tales are rich in character, plot, and theme. They originated in the oral tradition, as tales told around the fire to delight listeners but also to convey serious moral lessons. Most cultures have folk tales that go back hundreds, even thousands, of years. Yet these tales have characters and themes that remain relevant even today. Folk tales are the true predecessors of the short story form.*

*The following tale is part of the Balkan oral tradition, but similar stories are found in many other cultures.*

# The Maiden Wiser Than the Tsar

*Traditional tale retold by Idries Shah*

ONCE UPON A TIME THERE WAS A poor man who had one daughter.

Now, this girl was amazingly wise, seemed to have knowledge far beyond her years, and often said things which surprised her own father.

One day, being without a penny, the poor man went to the Tsar to beg.

The Tsar, astonished at the man's cultivated way of saying things, asked him where he had learned such phrases.

"From my daughter," he replied.

"But where was your daughter taught?" asked the Tsar.

"God and our poverty have made her wise," was the answer.

"Here is some money for your immediate needs," said the Tsar, "and here are thirty eggs; command your daughter in my name to hatch them for me. If she does this successfully, you shall both have rich presents, but if she does not, you will be put to the torture."

The man went home and took the eggs to his daughter. She examined them, and weighed one or two in her hands. Then she realised that they were hard-boiled. So, she said "Father, wait until tomorrow, maybe I can think what can be done about this."

Next day, she was up early, having thought of a solution, and boiled some beans. She gave her father a small bag of the beans, and said:

"Go with the plough and oxen, father, and start ploughing beside the road where the Tsar will pass on his way to church. When he puts his head out of the carriage window, call out 'Go on, good oxen, plough the land so that these boiled beans will grow well!'"

The father did as she told him, and sure enough, the Tsar put his head out of the window of his carriage to watch the man at work, and, hearing what was being shouted, said "Stupid Fellow, how can you expect boiled beans to produce anything?"

Primed by his daughter, the simple man called out, "Just as from boiled eggs chickens can be produced!"

So, laughing, the Tsar went on his way, knowing that the girl had outwitted him.

But it was not to end there.

The next day the Tsar sent a courtier to the poor man with a bundle of flax, saying "This flax must be made into sails for my ship by tomorrow; otherwise, you will be executed."

Weeping, the man went home, but his daughter said "Have no fear, I shall think of something."

In the morning she came to him and gave him a small block of wood, and said "Tell the Tsar that if he can have all the tools necessary for spinning and weaving made out of this piece of wood, I will do the material for his sails out of the bunch of flax."

He did so, and the Tsar was further impressed by the girl's answer. But he put a small glass into the man's hand and said:

"Go, take this to your daughter, and ask her to empty the sea with this so that I may enlarge my dominions with precious new pastures."

The man went home, and gave his daughter the glass, telling her that the ruler had demanded yet another impossibility.

"Go to bed!" she said, "I will think of something by bringing my mind to bear upon it all night."

In the morning she said "Go to the Tsar and tell him that if he can dam up all the rivers of the world with this bundle of tow, then I will empty the sea for him."

The father went back to the Tsar and told him what his daughter had said. The Tsar, seeing that she was wiser than himself, asked that she be brought to court forthwith. When she appeared he asked her:

"What is it that can be heard at the greatest distance?" Without any hesitation she replied at once:

"The thunder and the lie can be heard at the greatest distance,

O Tsar." Astonished, the Tsar grasped his beard, and then, turning to his courtiers asked:

"What is my beard worth, do you think?" Each of them began to say what they thought the Tsar's beard was worth, making the value higher and higher, hoping to curry favour with His Majesty. Then, he said to the maiden:

"And what do *you* think my beard is worth, my child?" Everyone looked on in amazement as she replied:

"Your Majesty's beard is worth every bit as much as three summer rains!" The Tsar, greatly astonished, said:

"You have guessed rightly; I shall marry you and make you my wife this very day." So the girl became the Tsarina. But just when the wedding was over, she said to the Tsar:

"I have one request to make; be graciously pleased to write with your own hand that if you, or anyone in your court be displeased with me, and I had to go away, I should be allowed to take with me any one thing which I liked best." Enamoured of the beautiful maiden, the Tsar asked for pen and parchment, and at once wrote, sealing the document with his own ruby ring, as she had requested.

The years passed most happily for both of them, then one day the Tsar had a heated argument with the Tsarina and said:

"Go, I desire that you leave this palace, never to return!"

"I shall go tomorrow, then," said the young Tsarina dutifully. "Only allow me one more night here to prepare myself for the journey home." The Tsar agreed, and she gave him his bedtime herbal drink with her usual care.

No sooner had the Tsar drunk the potion than he fell asleep. The Tsarina had the Tsar carried to a coach, and they went to her father's cottage.

When the morning came, the Tsar, who had spent a tranquil night, woke, and looked around him in amazement.

"Treason!" he roared, "Where am I, and whose prisoner?"

"Mine, your Majesty," said the Tsarina sweetly, "Your parchment, written with your own hand is here," and she showed him where he had written that if she had to leave the palace she could take with her that which she liked best.

Hearing this, the Tsar laughed heartily, and declared that his affection for her had returned. "My great love for you, O Tsar," said she "has made me do this bold thing, but I risked death to do it, so you must see that my love is indeed very great."

Then they were united, and lived happily together for the rest of their lives. ❧

**Idries Shah** (1924–1996) was born in India but lived much of his life in England. He was fascinated by cross-cultural studies, and collected and published stories and tales from many different cultures. His many books about Sufi spirituality were his best-known works, and helped to spread knowledge of some aspects of Islamic thought to readers in the West.

1. *Response*
   **a.** In addition to being entertaining, many folk tales express a moral lesson. What lesson or reminder does "The Maiden Wiser Than the Tsar" provide?
   **b.** Create a line graph to represent the plot of this tale in a visual way. Your graph should somehow indicate the various complications that arise, as well as the turning point of the story. Compare your graph with someone else's. Did you use similar or different approaches?

2. *Literature Studies* *Elements of Folklore* There are thousands of different folk tales, but they have many elements in common. Working in a group, identify elements in "The Maiden Wiser Than the Tsar" that appear in other folk tales with which you are familiar. Compare your ideas with those of other groups. If it is true that folk tales from around the world share common elements, what inferences might you make?

3. *Writing* *Modern Folk Tale* Write an updated version of "The Maiden Wiser Than the Tsar" using a modern setting and characters. You are free to change the details of all the impossible tasks set by the Tsar.

4. *Oral Language* *Presentation* Research the folklore of a culture that interests you. Prepare a presentation in which you summarize the unique or interesting aspects of that culture's folk tales. Complete your presentation with a dramatic reading of one tale.

# The Storyteller

## By Saki

*Have you ever been annoyed by noisy children on a long trip? Here's one man's solution.*

It was a hot afternoon, and the railway carriage was correspondingly sultry, and the next stop was at Templecombe, nearly an hour ahead. The occupants of the carriage were a small girl, and a smaller girl, and a small boy. An aunt belonging to the children occupied one corner seat, and the further corner seat on the opposite side was occupied by a bachelor who was a stranger to their party, but the small girls and the small boy emphatically occupied the compartment. Both the aunt and the children were conversational in a limited, persistent way, reminding one of the attentions of a housefly that refused to be discouraged. Most of the aunt's remarks seemed to begin with "Don't," and nearly all of the children's remarks began with "Why?" The bachelor said nothing out loud.

"Don't, Cyril, don't," exclaimed the aunt, as the small boy began smacking the cushions of the seat, producing a cloud of dust at each blow.

"Come and look out of the window," she added.

The child moved reluctantly to the window.

"Why are those sheep being driven out of that field?" he asked.

"I expect they are being driven to another field where there is more grass," said the aunt weakly.

"But there is lots of grass in that field," protested the boy. "There's nothing else but grass there. Aunt, there's lots of grass in that field."

"Perhaps the grass in the other field is better," suggested the aunt fatuously.

"Why is it better?" came the swift, inevitable question.

"Oh, look at those cows!" exclaimed the aunt. Nearly every field along the line had contained cows or bullocks, but she spoke as though she were drawing attention to a rarity.

"Why is the grass in the other field better?" persisted Cyril.

The frown on the bachelor's face was deepening to a scowl. He was a hard, unsympathetic man, the aunt decided in her mind. She was utterly unable to come to any satisfactory decision about the grass in the other field.

The smaller girl created a diversion by beginning to recite "On the Road to Mandalay." She only knew the first line, but she put her limited knowledge to the fullest possible use. She repeated the line over and over again in a dreamy but resolute and very audible voice; it seemed to the bachelor as though someone had had a bet with her that she could not repeat the line aloud two thousand times without stopping. Whoever it was who had made the wager was likely to lose his bet.

"Come over here and listen to a story," said the aunt, when the bachelor had looked twice at her and once at the communication cord.

The children moved listlessly toward the aunt's end of the carriage. Evidently her reputation as a storyteller did not rank high in their estimation.

In a low, confidential voice, interrupted at frequent intervals by loud, petulant questions from her listeners, she began an unenterprising and deplorably uninteresting story about a little girl who was good, and made friends with everyone on account of her goodness, and was finally saved from a mad bull by a number of rescuers who admired her moral character.

"Wouldn't they have saved her if she hadn't been good?" demanded the bigger of the small girls. It was exactly the question that the bachelor had wanted to ask.

"Well, yes," admitted the aunt lamely, "but I don't think they would have run quite so fast to her help if they had not liked her so much."

"It's the stupidest story I've ever heard," said the bigger of the small girls, with immense conviction.

"I didn't listen after the first bit, it was so stupid," said Cyril.

The smaller girl made no actual comment on the story, but she had long ago recommenced a murmured repetition of her favourite line.

"You don't seem to be a success as a storyteller," said the bachelor suddenly from his corner.

The aunt bristled in instant defence at this unexpected attack.

"It's a very difficult thing to tell stories that children can both understand and appreciate," she said stiffly.

"I don't agree with you," said the bachelor.

"Perhaps *you* would like to tell them a story," was the aunt's retort.

"Tell us a story," demanded the bigger of the small girls.

> The universe is made up of stories, not of atoms.
> Muriel Rukeyser

"Once upon a time," began the bachelor, "there was a little girl called Bertha, who was extraordinarily good."

The children's momentarily aroused interest began at once to flicker; all stories seemed dreadfully alike, no matter who told them.

"She did all that she was told, she was always truthful, she kept her clothes clean, ate milk puddings as though they were jam tarts, learned her lessons perfectly, and was polite in her manners."

"Was she pretty?" asked the bigger of the small girls.

"Not as pretty as any of you," said the bachelor, "but she was horribly good."

There was a wave of reaction in favor of the story; the word *horrible* in connection with goodness was a novelty that commended itself. It seemed to introduce a ring of truth that was absent from the aunt's tales of infant life.

"She was so good," continued the bachelor, "that she won several medals for goodness, which she always wore pinned onto her dress. There was a medal for obedience, another medal for punctuality, and a third for good behaviour. They were large metal medals, and they clicked against one another as she walked. No other child in the town where she lived had as many as three medals, so everybody knew that she must be an extra good child."

"Horribly good," quoted Cyril.

"Everybody talked about her goodness, and the Prince of the country got to hear about it, and he said that as she was so very good she might be allowed once a week to walk in his park, which was just outside the town. It was a beautiful park, and no children were ever allowed in it, so it was a great honour for Bertha to be allowed to go there."

"Were there any sheep in the park?" demanded Cyril.

"No," said the bachelor, "there were no sheep."

"Why weren't there any sheep?" came the inevitable question arising out of that answer.

The aunt permitted herself a smile, which might almost have been described as a grin.

"There were no sheep in the park," said the bachelor, "because the Prince's mother had once had a dream that her son would either be killed by a sheep or else by a clock falling on him. For that reason the Prince never kept a sheep in his park or a clock in his palace."

The aunt suppressed a gasp of admiration.

"Was the Prince killed by a sheep or by a clock?" asked Cyril.

"He is still alive, so we can't tell whether the dream will come true," said the bachelor unconcernedly. "Anyway, there were no sheep in the park, but there were lots of little pigs running all over the place."

"What colour were they?"

"Black with white faces, white with black spots, black all over, grey with white patches, and some were white all over."

The storyteller paused to let the full idea of the park's treasures sink into the children's imaginations; then he resumed:

"Bertha was rather sorry to find that there were no flowers in the park. She had promised her aunts, with tears in her eyes, that she would not pick any of the kind Prince's flowers, and she had meant to keep her promise, so of course it made her feel silly to find that there were no flowers to pick."

"Why weren't there any flowers?"

"Because the pigs had eaten them all," said the bachelor promptly. "The gardeners had told the Prince that you couldn't have pigs and flowers, so he decided to have pigs and no flowers."

There was a murmur of approval at the excellence of the Prince's decision; so many people would have decided the other way.

"There were lots of other delightful things in the park. There were ponds with gold and blue and green fish in them, and trees with beautiful parrots that said clever things at a moment's notice, and humming birds that hummed all the popular tunes of the day. Bertha walked up and down and enjoyed herself immensely, and thought to herself, 'If I were not so extraordinarily good I should not have been allowed to come into this beautiful park and enjoy all there is to be seen in it,' and her three medals clinked against one another as she walked and helped to remind her how very good she really was. Just then an enormous wolf came prowling into the park to see if it could catch a fat little pig for its supper."

"What colour was it?" asked the children, amid an immediate quickening of interest.

"Mud-colour all over, with a black tongue and pale grey eyes that gleamed with unspeakable ferocity. The first thing that it saw in the park was Bertha; her pinafore[1] was so spotlessly white and clean that it could be seen from a great distance. Bertha saw the wolf and saw that it was stealing toward her, and she began to wish that she had never been allowed to come into the park. She ran as hard as she could, and the wolf came after her with huge leaps and bounds. She managed to reach a shrubbery of myrtle bushes, and she hid herself in one of the thickest of the bushes. The wolf came sniffing among the branches, its black tongue lolling out of its mouth and its pale grey eyes glaring with rage.

---

[1]**pinafore:** a sleeveless dress

Bertha was terribly frightened, and thought to herself: 'If I had not been so extraordinarily good, I should have been safe in town at this moment.'

"However, the scent of the myrtle was so strong that the wolf could not sniff out where Bertha was hiding, and the bushes were so thick that he might have hunted about in them for a long time without catching sight of her; so he thought he might as well go off and catch a little pig instead. Bertha was trembling very much at having the wolf prowling and sniffing so near her, and as she trembled the medal for obedience clinked against the medals for good conduct and punctuality. The wolf was just moving away when he heard the sound of the medals clinking and stopped to listen; they clinked again in a bush quite near him. He dashed into the bush, his pale grey eyes gleaming with ferocity and triumph, and dragged Bertha out and devoured her to the last morsel. All that was left of her were her shoes, bits of clothing, and the three medals for goodness."

"Were any of the little pigs killed?"

"No, they all escaped."

"The story began badly," said the smaller of the two girls, "but it had a beautiful ending."

"It is the most beautiful story that I ever heard," said the bigger of the small girls, with immense decision.

"It is the *only* beautiful story I have ever heard," said Cyril.

A dissentient opinion came from the aunt.

"A most improper story to tell to young children! You have undermined the effect of years of careful teaching."

"At any rate," said the bachelor, collecting his belongings preparatory to leaving the carriage, "I kept them quiet for ten minutes, which was more than you were able to do."

"Unhappy woman!" he observed to himself as he walked down the platform of Templecombe station. "For the next six months or so those children will assail her in public with demands for an improper story!"

**Saki** (1870–1916) was the pen name of Hector Hugh Munro. He was born in Burma, but spent most of his childhood in England. Best known as a short story writer, Munro was also a satirist and a journalist.
His career as a writer was promising but brief. When World War I began in 1914 he enlisted as a soldier. On the 14th of November, 1916, while stationed in France, he was killed by a sniper.
"The Storyteller" was first published in 1914.

## 1. Response

**a.** What are the first lines in the story that suggest "The Storyteller" is meant to be humorous?

**b.** When and where do you think "The Storyteller" takes place? List some specific words and phrases that help the reader draw conclusions about the setting.

**c.** The aunt's story is *didactic*—its purpose is to teach a moral lesson. How do the children react to her story? Why?

**d.** Reflect on your own reading and viewing habits. What kinds of stories do you prefer? Why? What do you think of works whose purpose is to illustrate that virtue and goodness are rewarded?

## 2. *Oral Language* Group Discussion

Long ago, all stories were spoken aloud to the audience. As a group, discuss where stories are found today and how they are delivered. Which methods of storytelling do you prefer? Explain.

## 3. *Literature Studies* Principles of Storytelling

Reread "The Storyteller" carefully and create five guidelines for storytelling that the bachelor would accept. Are these guidelines enough, or do you think more are required? Why?

# Bluffing

## By Gail Helgason

*"In the end, Gabriella felt she'd fooled them all. Oh, she'd answered all the questions, but that wasn't the same as telling the whole story."*

She reaches for her double-faced pile jacket in the hallway, opens the front door, and runs down the sidewalk as fast as she dares. It's only three blocks to the Jasper hospital. Wind-driven rivers of ice have formed on the hospital steps and Gabriella almost loses her footing. She grips the railing. She wonders what her grade ten students would think if they could see her, clutching the rail, as if the slightest breeze could blow her down.

Inside the hospital, equilibrium returns. The tiled floor feels cold, even through her vibram soles. The hospital is modern and all on one level. The corridors are eggshell white, full of promise, Gabriella thinks. She would have preferred vomit green. Even the reassuring medicinal smell seems diluted. The scent reminds her of the home-made cleaning solution she prepared at Liam's insistence. She used the mixture for a week, until she noticed that it took twice as long to remove grime as the concentrate she bought at the janitorial supply store. Liam hadn't noticed that she'd stopped using it.

The nurse at the station nods to Gabriella. "It will just be a few minutes," she says. "Won't you have a seat?" She can't be more than twenty-two, thinks Gabriella, three years younger than she is. She sinks into the vinyl couch. Only three weeks since the accident, and it seems as if she's been waiting forever.

On that morning three weeks ago, a light frost had silvered the club-moss along the trail. Ahead, the plum-coloured peaks of the Maligne Range cut razor-sharp silhouettes against the sky. Gabriella noticed how Liam's thick black hair was cut as fashionably as ever, unusual for a climber, although his face appeared lined and travel-worn.

Gabriella hadn't proposed the hike until the night before. She'd called it "one last outing before the snow comes." She didn't want to let on that it might mean anything much to her. At the lake, she planned to bring up the subject of the lease. The landlord said he'd have to know by October 31 if they would sign for a year. Housing was so tight in Jasper; he had at least three people who would take the house sight unseen. Would they sign the lease or not? He always speaks to her about these matters, not Liam.

The morning sky began to cream with cumulus clouds. Below, in the valley, the dark greens of white spruce and tarnished golds of the poplars wove an intricate montane tartan.

Liam stayed in the lead. At times, Gabriella had to run, the way her students sometimes did to keep up with her on field trips to nearby bogs and meadows. But she didn't mind Liam's pace. She sensed a special energy to the day. They'd be able to firm things up at the lake, the way they never could in town, knocking elbows, rushing about. She couldn't take the uncertainty much longer, now that Liam was talking about going off again for the winter, and she couldn't afford to keep the house herself. She thought that signing a one-year lease demanded a certain courage, a certain faith that the earth will keep holding them up, a certain commitment. She planned to introduce the subject in this way, as a challenge.

"Should get the lake all to ourselves," Liam said.

His boots left the partial prints of an expensive trademark on the soft loamy trail. His jacket was new, too. He spent most of his money on outdoor gear—the little he made guiding American and German tourists up easy climbs in the Rockies. Liam liked to joke that one day he would have his photo in glossy magazines for high-tech outdoor gear. Prestigious companies would seek his endorsement. He always laughed when he said this, but there was a steel edge to his voice. He really believed it. She thought he was getting a little long in the tooth for this kind of fantasy.

When they were half-way to the lake, they stopped for a short break on a fallen log. They heard a man's laughter from somewhere below. Liam turned to Gabriella, his eyes vigilant. She had seen that expression once before, when Clive, one of the other mountain guides in the town, asked Liam if the rumours were true. Had he almost lost his nerve on Mt. Robson last year, when he realized the American climber he was guiding couldn't set up a belay that gave Liam adequate protection? Liam told Clive to go to hell. But Liam was secretly jealous of Clive. Liam has never been asked to join a big expedition; Clive was invited to Mt. McKinley last year.

"I'll handle it," Liam whispered.

Two young men approached. They looked to be in their late teens or early twenties. They took big elastic steps, as if springs were attached to the soles of their boots. Grey jays emitted staccato cries into the spruce air.

"Planning on going up to the lake?" Liam asked.

"You bet," one of them replied.

"Might not be such a good idea," Liam said, his voice thick with sympathy. "We're turning back ourselves. Came across an elk carcass by the lake. Some grizzly had himself a dandy breakfast."

"Grizzly, eh?" said the hiker. "Sure it was a grizzly?"

"Can't mistake those long front claws," Liam said. "They usually come back to the kill, you know."

"Guess you're right. Doesn't sound like a great place to be."

The pair turned around on the trail; the spring was missing from their step. When they were out of sight, Liam and Gabriella continued on to the lake. The grey jays had stopped shrieking.

Gabriella hears footsteps in the hospital corridor and looks up from a *Canadian Living* magazine to see the young nurse coming out of Liam's room.

"He's sleeping but I'll wake him in a minute," she says. Gabriella thinks she catches a quizzical look on her face. The nurse seems to be weighing whether to say anything more, then shows her straight teeth in a smile. "He really wants you to be here today, doesn't he?"

Gabriella nods. She doesn't know what to say. The nurse leaves her and pads down the corridor. Gabriella draws her legs under her. Her feet still feel icy.

Tell us what happened, the strangers said, pressing in on her with their uniforms, badges, khaki jackets, and pressed pants. All of them urged her to tell. "To aid in our understanding of how these attacks occur," said one warden, a safety specialist, with a smooth chin and a particularly insistent manner.

In the end, Gabriella felt she'd fooled them all. Oh, she'd answered all the questions, but that wasn't the same as telling the whole story. How could she, when it still wasn't clear?

Gabriella watches as a merlin alights on a bare branch outside the window. Odd that he'd get so close. Then she sees the streaky yellow plumage. Just a baby. He thinks the world is a nurturing place.

Where is that nurse?

Gabriella looks again at the merlin and remembers how she taught Liam to spot wildlife. He said he hadn't really taken much notice up till then, his eyes were always on the peaks. But he wanted to know more. This was after they'd moved in together, before he'd gone off to Leavenworth with Clive for two weeks' climbing that turned into six weeks.

She and Liam had been looking for wildlife up on the Pyramid Bench. Liam couldn't see anything. Gabriella said the problem was that he was trying to focus on a single object. Instead, he should try to soften his eyes and take in the entire horizon. Liam tried this. He wasn't always willing to learn from people who might know more than he did, but she hoped he'd recognize her authority here. After all, she was the biology teacher.

They crouched behind a stand of young spruce. In a few minutes, they observed movement at the edge of the forest: a cow moose, holding her head high, ears up instead of out.

"Means she senses danger," Gabriella said. "She probably has a calf around here. Better freeze. The worst thing to do would be to run."

They both froze. Afterwards, Liam said he'd learned a lot being out with her. It opened his eyes, he said.

At noon, Gabriella and Liam reached the lake. She found a rock of flat limestone along the shore and they spread their foam pads to sit on. Liam dug into his pack and pulled out a small bottle of Remy Martin, French bread, a wedge of Camembert, and chocolate-covered almonds.

She felt a small rush of pleasure. He never lost the ability to surprise her, sometimes through astonishing small deceits, sometimes through extravagant gestures. In a way he reminded her of the plants and animals she so loved teaching her students about: organized, coded, identifiable as a type, but ultimately unknowable. Gabriella decided not to mention the foil-wrapped egg sandwiches in her day pack; she wouldn't dream of spoiling his surprise.

"To celebrate," Liam said. He didn't say right away what they would be celebrating, but Gabriella took this as an encouraging sign. She planned to mention the lease after lunch. She imagined winter nights with Liam hunkered over topographical maps at the yellow kitchen table. Only this time, she saw him studying places they could explore together, high meadows and alpine lakes. She smiled up at him.

"Clive and I worked it out last week," Liam said. He shook his crop of black hair and his voice pranced. "If we pool our resources, live in his old van, we've got just enough to get by for three months over the winter. So we're gonna head down south."

The words hit Gabriella like small, sharp rocks.

"I've had enough of this limestone," Liam continued. "Three months of good, technical rock—I'm talking Yosemite, maybe New

Mexico—is gonna make all the difference for me."

Gabriella grabbed for her pack and pushed herself off the rock. She strode as fast as she could without running. She didn't care where. Once she looked back. Liam was following her. Let him hoof it a little, she thought. She willed herself to walk fast and stay angry, because she didn't want to think about what might happen to her if she relented one more time. Maybe there would be nothing left of her except endurance, maybe all her other strengths would be sucked away. She'd seen it happen.

The sandy shore of the lake ended and Gabriella crashed through a thick stand of dwarf birch and rock willows. A twig snapped and cut into her cheek. She hauled herself through one last bush to the end of the lake, where the willows gave way to huckleberries.

The grizzly sow stood twenty paces ahead. The bear's hump and dished-in face were unmistakable. There was not a climbing tree within reach.

In that instant, every cell in Gabriella's body yearned to turn and flee. But some inner force held her, a force she'd never before sensed.

Gabriella dropped her eyes from the bear's stare and slumped her body forwards. She noticed how scuffed her boots were. She knew that if she retreated too quickly, the bear could be on her like a cat on a wounded bumblebee. She tried moving one foot back. The bear stepped forwards a foot or two. Gabriella froze. The bear stopped.

Behind her, she heard rustling in the shrubbery, and then Liam's voice. "Geez," he said.

It took all her willpower to stay where she was. "Try backing off slowly," she said. "Bluff him, remember?"

And now, as Gabriella sits on the hospital couch, the part that was missing comes back. How she waited to hear Liam take one or two cautious steps backwards. How instead, after one long minute, she heard the rustle of footsteps through shrubbery. Liam wasn't just stepping back. He was running away as fast as he could.

Gabriella hit the ground as the bear lunged forwards. She intertwined her fingers behind her neck, legs drawn up over her vitals. But even as her forehead pressed against the gravelly earth, she felt the powerful sweep of the bear hurtling past. It was giving full chase.

The nurse is back. She bends down to Gabriella.

"He'll be counting on your reaction," she says. "Are you sure you feel up to it?"

Gabriella nods, but as she is ushered into Liam's private room, she is no longer so sure. He sits propped up in bed beside a table brimming with gladioli, carnations, cards from the climbing team. He looks a bit like pictures she has seen of mummified Egyptian princes. Bandages wind round his scalp, over his cheeks and forehead and chin. Only his blue eyes, nostrils, and mouth are visible.

What was it the doctor had told her after they airlifted him to the hospital? "No damage to the vital organs, that's the main thing." Then he'd listed the injuries. Gabriella had to bite down on her fist to keep from screaming.

"Gabriella," Liam whispers. She goes to his side. Broad beams of light penetrate the room from the west window and hurt her eyes.

"I'm here," she says. She places her palm lightly over one of his bandaged hands.

"I'm glad." Liam stares at her unflinchingly. "I thought you'd be here before this."

"I've been here every day for the last three weeks," Gabriella says. "You've been sleeping most of the time. It's just hard for you to remember."

"You know I wasn't trying to run away up there," Liam says. "You know that?"

"Of course."

"I meant the bear to come after me instead of you," he says.

Gabriella's mouth feels dry. She looks at her outstretched fingers, the irregular roof her knuckles and joints form over Liam's bandaged hand. She wonders if she could move her hand if she tries. For a moment, she hears Clive's accusing voice and the bear's low grunt.

The doctor sweeps into the room and the nurse announces that they are ready to begin. The nurse starts to snip at the facial bandage. Liam's forehead emerges, what is left of his eyebrows, just shadowy lines really, then his cheeks and chin. Beneath the bandages, the skin is all puffed up, mottled, with ridges of shiny, rubbery scar tissue criss-crossing like tributaries on a map. Gabriella's eyes linger on her feet.

When the last bandage is removed, she pulls her chair closer to the bed and stretches her lips into a smile. She knows in her bones that she can manage this way, for the rest of the afternoon, at least. She still has that much bluffing left in her.

**Gail Helgason** lives in Edmonton.
Her short story collection, *Fracture Patterns,* was shortlisted in 1996 for both the Writers Guild of Alberta Best First Book Award, and the City of Edmonton Book Prize.

**I. Response**

    **a.** In the first three paragraphs of the story, what concrete information did you learn about Gabriella? At that point, what inferences were you able to draw about the relationship between her and Liam?

    **b.** What was your first impression of Liam? What process did you use to arrive at this impression? Do you think this is the same process that people use in everyday life when they meet someone new?

    **c.** Explain how the title of the story is important to an understanding of the final scene between Gabriella and Liam.

    **d.** "Bluffing" focusses on a conflict between two characters. What is the essential conflict? In your view, does the story present the conflict neutrally? Explain.

**2. Literature Studies** *Foreshadowing* Reread the story and identify specific lines that **foreshadow** some aspect of the story's conclusion. Find further examples of foreshadowing in this unit and compare these stories.

**Foreshadowing** is a plot technique in which a writer plants clues or subtle indications about events that will happen later in the narrative.

**3. Language Conventions** *Verb Tenses* What two main verb tenses does the author, Gail Helgason, use to tell her story? In a group, discuss why verb tense is an important part of the story's structure. Compare Helgason's use of verb tense with Coakley's in "Mirror Image." What are some of the advantages and disadvantages of each approach?

**4. Research and Inquiry** Working in a group, use the Internet and other resources to learn more about encounters between grizzlies and humans. Begin by brainstorming at least five questions you would like to answer. When you have gathered the required information, present your findings to the class. Are the findings of the various groups consistent, or are there obvious differences? Explain how your own group determined the reliability of the resources you accessed.

# The Labrador Fiasco

By
Margaret
Atwood

"We left behind ...
one by one our civilized
distinctions

and entered a large darkness.

It was our own
ignorance we entered."
MARGARET ATWOOD, from
*The Journals of Susanna Moodie*

It's October, but which October? One of those Octobers with their quick intensities of light, their diminuendos, their red and orange leaves. My father is sitting in his armchair by the fire. He has on his black-and-white-checked dressing gown, over his other clothes, and his old leather slippers, with his feet propped up on a hassock. Therefore it must be evening.

My mother is reading to him. She fiddles with her glasses, and hunches over the page; or it looks like hunching. In fact, that is just the shape she is now.

My father is grinning, so this must be a part he enjoys. His grin is higher on the left side than on the right: six years ago he had a stroke, which we all pretend he's recovered from; and he has, mostly.

"What's happening now?" I say, taking off my coat. I already know the story, having heard it before.

"They've just set out," says my mother.

My father says, "They took the wrong supplies." This pleases him: he himself would not have taken the wrong supplies. In fact, he would never have gone on this ill-advised journey in the first place, or—although he was once more reckless, more impetuous, more sure of his ability to confront fate and transcend danger—this is his opinion now. "Darn fools," he says, grinning away.

But what supplies could they have taken, other than the wrong ones? White sugar, white flour, rice; that was what you took then. Peameal, sulphured apples, hardtack, bacon, lard. Heavy things. There was no freeze-drying then, no handy packaged soups; there were no nylon vests, no pocket-sized sleeping bags, no light-weight tarpaulins. Their tent was made of balloon silk, oiled to waterproof it. Their blankets were of wool. The packsacks were canvas, with leather straps and tumplines that went across the forehead to cut the strain on the back. They would have smelled of tar. In addition there were two rifles, two pistols, 1,200 rounds of ammunition, a camera, and a sextant; and then the cooking utensils and the clothing. Every pound of it had to be carried over each and every portage, or hauled upriver in the canoe, which was eighteen feet long, wood-framed, and canvas-covered.

None of this would have daunted the adventurers, however; or not at first. There were two of them, two young Americans; they'd been on camping expeditions before, although at warmer latitudes, with fragrant evening pipes smoked before cheerful blazes and a fresh-caught trout sizzling in the pan while the sunsets paled in the west. Each would have been able to turn a neat, Kiplingesque[1] paragraph or two on the lure of wild places, the challenge of the unknown. This was in 1903, when exploration was still in vogue as a test of manliness, and when manliness itself was still in vogue and was thought to couple naturally with the word *clean*. Manliness, cleanliness, the wilderness, where you could feel free. With gun and fishing rod, of course. You could live off the land.

The leader of the expedition, whose name was Hubbard, worked for a magazine dedicated to the outdoors. His idea was that he and his chum and cousin—whose name was Wallace—would penetrate the last unmapped Labrador wilds, and he would write a series of articles about their adventures, and thus make his name. (These were his very words: "I will make my name.") Specifically, they would ascend the Nascaupee River, said to flow out of Lake Michikamau, a fabled inland lake teeming with fish; from there they could make it to the George River, where the Indians congregated every summer for the caribou hunt, and from there to a Hudson's Bay post and out to the coast again. While among the Indians, Hubbard planned to do a little amateur anthropology, which he would also write up, with photographs—a shaggy-haired hunter with an old-fashioned rifle, his foot on a carcass; a cut-off head with spreading antlers; women with bead necklaces and gleaming eyes chewing the hide, or sewing it, or whatever they did.

---

[1]**Kiplingesque:** in the style of Rudyard Kipling, British writer

*The Last Wild People.* Something like that. There was a great interest in such subjects. He would describe the menus, too.

(But those Indians came from the north. No one ever took the river route from the west and south.)

In stories like this, there is always—there is supposed to be—an old Indian who appears to the white men as they are planning to set out. He comes to warn them, because he is kind at heart and they are ignorant. "Do not go there," he says. "That is a place we never go." Indians in these tales have a formal manner of speaking.

"Why not?" the white men say.

"Bad spirits live there," says the old Indian. The white men smile and thank him, and disregard his advice. Native superstition, they think. So they go where they've been warned not to, and then, after many hardships, they die. The old Indian shakes his head when he hears of it. Foolish white men, but what can you tell them? They have no respect.

There's no old Indian in this book—he somehow got left out—so my father takes the part upon himself. "They shouldn't have gone there," he says. "The Indians never went that way." He doesn't say *bad spirits*, however. He says, "Nothing to eat." For the Indians it would have been the same thing, because where does food come from if not from the spirits? It isn't just there, it is given; or else withheld.

Hubbard and Wallace tried to hire several Indians to come with them, at least on the first stages of the journey, and to help with the packs. None would go; they said they were "too busy." Really they knew too much. What they knew was that you couldn't possibly carry with you, in there, everything you would need to eat. And if you couldn't carry it, you would have to kill it. But most of the time there was nothing to kill. "Too busy" meant too busy to die. It also meant too polite to point out the obvious.

The two explorers did do one thing right. They hired a guide. His name was George, and he was a Cree Indian, or partly; what they called then a breed. He was from James Bay, too far away from Labrador to know the full and evil truth about it. George travelled south to meet his employers, all the way to New York City, where he had never been before. He had never been to the United States before, or even to a city. He kept calm; he looked about him; he demonstrated his resourcefulness by figuring out what a taxicab was and how to hire one. His ability to reason things through was to come in very handy later on.

"That George was quite a boy," says my father. George is his favourite person in the whole story.

Somewhere around the house there's a picture of my father himself

—at the back of a photo album, perhaps, with the snapshots that haven't yet been stuck in. It shows him thirty years younger, on some canoe trip or another—if you don't write these things down on the backs of the pictures, they get forgotten. He's evidently crossing a portage. He hasn't shaved, he's got a bandana tied around his head because of the blackflies and mosquitoes, and he's carrying a heavy pack, with the broad tumpline across his forehead. His hair is dark, his glistening face is deeply tanned and not what you'd call clean. He looks slightly villainous—like a pirate, or indeed like a northwoods guide, the kind who might suddenly vanish in the middle of the night, along with your best rifle, just before the wolves arrive on the scene. But like someone who knows what he's doing.

"That George knew what he was doing," says my father now.

Once he got out of New York, that is; while there, George wasn't much help, because he didn't know where to shop. It was in New York that the two men bought all the necessary supplies, except a gill net, which they thought they could find up north. They also failed to purchase extra moccasins. This may have been their worst mistake.

Then they set out, by train and then by boat and then by smaller boat. The details are tedious. The weather was bad, the meals were foul, none of the transportation was ever on time. They spent a lot of hours, and even days, waiting around on docks and wondering when their luggage would turn up.

"That's enough for tonight," says my mother.

"I think he's asleep," I say.

"He never used to go to sleep," says my mother. "Not with this story. Usually he's busy making up his list."

"His list?"

"His list of what he would take."

While my father sleeps, I skip ahead in the story. The three men have finally made it inland from the bleak northeastern shore of Labrador, and have left their last jumping-off place, and are voyaging in earnest.

It's the middle of July, but the short summer will soon be over, and they have five hundred miles to go.

Their task is to navigate Grand Lake, which is long and thin; at its extreme end, or so they've been told, the Nascaupee flows into it. The only map they've seen, crudely drawn by an earlier white traveller some fifty years before, shows Grand Lake with only one river emptying into it. One is all the Indians have ever mentioned: the one that goes somewhere. Why talk about the others, because why would anyone want to know about them? There are many plants that have no names because they cannot be eaten or used.

But in fact there are four other rivers.

During this first morning they are exhilarated, or so Wallace records. Their hopes are high, adventure calls. The sky is deep blue, the air is crisp, the sun is bright, the treetops seem to beckon them on. They do not know enough to beware of beckoning treetops. For lunch they have flapjacks and syrup, and are filled with a sense of well-being. They know they're going into danger, but they also know that they are immortal. Such moods do occur, in the North. They take pictures with their camera: of their laden canoe; of one another—moustached, be-sweatered, with puttee-shaped wrappings on their legs and things on their heads that look like bowler hats—leaning blithely on their pad-dles. Heartbreaking, but only when you know the end. As it is they're having the time of their lives.

There's another photo of my father, perhaps from the same trip as the one with the portage; or he's wearing the same bandana. This time he's grinning into the camera lens, pretending to shave himself with his axe. Two tall-tale points are being made: that his axe is as sharp as a razor, and that his bristles are so tough that only an axe could cut them. It's highjinks, a canoe-trip joke; although secretly, of course, he once believed both of these things.

On the second day the three men pass the mouth of the Nascau-pee, which is hidden behind an island and looks like shoreline. They don't even suspect it is there. They continue on to the end of the lake, and enter the river they find there. They've taken the wrong turn.

I don't get back to Labrador for more than a week. When I return, it's a Sunday night. The fire is blazing away and my father is sitting in front of it, waiting to see what will happen next. My mother is rustling up the baking-powder biscuits and the decaffeinated tea. I forage for cookies.

"How is everything?" I say.

"Fine," she says. "But he doesn't get enough exercise." *Everything* means my father, as far as she is concerned.

"You should make him go for a walk," I say.

"*Make* him," she says.

"Well, suggest."

"He doesn't see the point of walking just to walk," she says. "If you're not going anywhere."

"You could send him on errands," I say. To this she does not bother even to reply.

"He says his feet hurt," she says. I think of the array of almost-new boots and shoes in the cupboard; boots and shoes that have proliferated lately. He keeps buying other ones. If only he can find the right pair, he must think, whatever it is that's causing his feet to hurt will go away.

I carry in the teacups, dole out the plates. "So, how are Hubbard and Wallace coming along?" I say. "Have you got to the place where they eat the owl?"

"Slim pickings," he says. "They took the wrong river. Even if they'd found the right one, it was too late to start."

Hubbard and Wallace and George toil upstream. The heat at midday is oppressive. Flies torment them, little flies like pinpricks, giant ones as big as your thumb. The river is barely navigable: they have to haul their laden canoe over gravel shallows, or portage around rapids, through forest that is harsh and unmarked and jumbled. In front of them the river unrolls; behind them it closes up like a maze. The banks of the river grow steeper; hill after hill, gentle in outline, hard at the core. It's a sparse landscape: ragged spruce, birch, aspen, all spindly; in some places burned over, the way forward blocked by charred and fallen tree trunks.

How long is it before they realize they've gone up the wrong river? Far too long. They cache some of their food so they won't have to carry it; they throw some of it away. They manage to shoot a caribou, which they eat, leaving the hoofs and head behind. Their feet hurt; their moccasins are wearing out.

At last Hubbard climbs a high hill, and from its top he sees Lake Michikamau; but the river they have been following does not go there. The lake is too far away; they can't possibly haul their canoe that far through the forest. They will have to turn back.

In the evening their talk is no longer of discovery and exploration. Instead they talk about what they will eat. What they'll eat tomorrow, and what they'll eat when they get back. They compose bills of fare, feasts, grand blowouts. George is able to shoot or catch this and that. A duck here, a grouse there. A whisky-jack. They catch sixty trout, painstakingly one by one, using a hook and line because they have no gill net. The trout are clear and fresh as icewater, but only six inches long. Nothing is nearly enough. The work of travelling uses up more energy than they can take in; they are slowly dissolving, wasting away.

> The answers you get from literature depend on
> the questions you pose.
>
> Hannah Arendt

Meanwhile, the nights become longer and longer and darker and darker. Ice forms on the edges of the river. Hauling the canoe over the shallows, through the rushing, stone cold water, leaves them shivering and gasping. The first snowflurries fall.

"It's rough country," says my father. "No moose; not even bears. That's always a bad sign, no bears." He's been there, or near it; same sort of terrain. He speaks of it with admiration and nostalgia, and a kind of ruefulness. "Now, of course, you can fly in. You can cover their whole route in a couple of hours." He waves his fingers dismissively. So much for planes.

"What about the owl?" I say.

"What owl?" says my father.

"The one they ate," I say. "I think it's where the canoe dumps, and they save their matches by sticking them in their ears."

"I think that was the others," says my father. "The ones who tried the same thing later. I don't think this bunch ate an owl."

"If they had eaten one, what sort of owl would it have been?" I say.

"Great horned or boreal," he says, "if they were lucky. More meat on those. But it may have been something smaller." He gives a series of thin, eerie barks, like a dog at a distance, and then he grins. He knows every bird up there by its call; he still does.

"He's sleeping too much in the afternoons," says my mother.

"Maybe he's tired," I say.

"He shouldn't be that tired," she says. "Tired, and restless as well. He's losing his appetite."

"Maybe he needs a hobby," I say. "Something to occupy his mind."

"He used to have a lot of them," my mother says.

I wonder where they've all gone, those hobbies. Their tools and materials are still around: the plane and the spirit level, the feathers for tying dry flies, the machine for enlarging prints, the points for making arrows. These bits and pieces seem to me like artifacts, the kind that are dug up at archaeological sites, and then pondered over and classified, and used for deducing the kind of life once lived.

"He used to say he wanted to write his memoirs," says my mother. "A sort of account; all the places he's been. He did begin it several times, but now he's lost interest. He can't see too well."

"He could use a tape recorder," I say.

"Oh, help," says my mother. "More gadgets!"

The winds howl and cease, the snow falls and stops falling. The three men have traversed across to a different river, hoping it will be better, but it isn't. One night George has a dream: God appears to him, shining and bright and affable, and speaks in a manner that is friendly but firm. "I can't spare any more of these trout," he says, "but if you stick to this river you'll get down to Grand Lake all right. Just you don't leave the river, and I'll get you out safe."

George tells the others of his dream. It is discounted. The men abandon their canoe and strike out overland, hoping to reach their old trail. After far too long they do reach it, and stumble along it down the valley of the river they first ascended, rummaging through their former campsites for any food they might have thrown away. They aren't counting in miles, but in days; how many days they have left, and how many it will take. But that will depend on the weather, and on their own strength; how fast they can go. They find a lump of mouldering flour, a bit of lard, a few bones, some caribou hoofs, which they boil. A little tin of dry mustard; they mix it into the soup, and find it encouraging.

In the third week of October, this is how things stand:

Hubbard has become too weak to go any farther. He's been left behind, wrapped in his blankets, in the tent, with a fire going. The other two have gone on; they hope to walk out, then send help back for him. He's given them the last of the peameal.

The snow is falling. For dinner he has some strong tea and bone broth, and some boiled rawhide, made from the last of his moccasins; he writes in his journal that it is truly delicious. Now he is without foot-gear. He has every hope that the others will succeed, and will return and save him; or so he records. Nevertheless, he begins a farewell message for his wife. He writes that he has a pair of cowhide mittens that he is looking forward to cooking and eating the next day.

After that he goes to sleep, and after that he dies.

Some days farther down the trail, Wallace too has to give up. He and George part company: Wallace intends to go back with the latest leavings they've managed to locate—a few handfuls of mouldy flour. He will find Hubbard, and together they will await rescue. But he's been caught in a blizzard, and has lost his bearings; at the moment he's in a shelter made of branches, waiting for the snow to let up. He is amazingly weak, and no longer hungry, which he knows is a bad sign. Every movement he makes is slow and deliberate, and at the same time unreal, as if his body is apart from him and he is only watching it. In the white light of day or the red flicker of the fire—for he still has fire—the patterns on the ends of his own fingers appear miraculous to him. Such clarity and detail; he follows the pattern of the woven blanket as if tracing a map.

His dead wife has appeared to him, and has given him several pieces of practical advice concerning his sleeping arrangement: a thicker layer of spruce boughs underneath, she's said, would be more comfortable. Sometimes he only hears her; sometimes he sees her as well. She's wearing a blue summer dress, her long hair pinned up in a shining coil. She appears perfectly at home; the poles of the shelter are visible through her back. Wallace has ceased to be surprised by this.

Even farther along, George continues to walk; to walk out. He knows more or less where he's going; he will find help and return with it. But he isn't out yet, he's still in. Snow surrounds him, the blank grey sky enfolds him; at one point he comes across his own tracks and realizes he's been walking in a circle. He too is thin and weak, but he's managed to shoot a porcupine. He pauses to think it through: he could turn around, retrace his steps, take the porcupine back to share with the others; or he could eat all of it himself and go forward. He knows that if he goes back it's likely that none of them will get out alive; but if he goes on, there's at least a possibility, at least for him. He goes on, hoarding the bones.

"That George did the right thing," says my father.

While sitting at the dinner table my father has another stroke. This time it knocks out half the vision in each eye, his short-term memory, and his sense of where he is. From one minute to the next, he has become lost; he gropes through the living room as if he's never been in such a place before. The doctors say this time it's unlikely he'll recover.

Time passes. Now the lilacs are in bloom outside the window, and he can see them, or parts of them. Despite this he thinks it's October. Still, the core of him is still there. He sits in his armchair, trying to figure things out. One sofa cushion looks much like another unless you have something to go by. He watches the sunlight gleaming on the hardwood floor; his best guess is that it's a stream. In extreme situations you have to use your wits.

"I'm here," I say, kissing his dry cheek. He hasn't gone bald, not in the least. He has silvery white hair, like an egret frozen.

He peers at me out of the left sides of his eyes, which are the ones that work. "You seem to have become very old all of a sudden," he says.

As far as we can tell, he's missing the last four or five years, and several blocks of time before that as well. He's disappointed in me: not because of anything I've done, but because of what I've failed to do. I've failed to remain young. If I could have managed that, I could have saved him; then he too could have remained as he was.

I wish I could think of something to amuse him. I've tried recordings of bird songs, but he doesn't like them: they remind him that there's something he once knew, but can't remember. Stories are no good, not even short ones, because by the time you get to the second page he's forgotten the beginning. Where are we without our plots?

Music is better; it takes place drop by drop.

My mother doesn't know what to do, and so she rearranges: cups and plates, documents, bureau drawers. Right now she's outside, yanking weeds out of the garden in a bewildered frenzy. Dirt and couch grass fly through the air: that at least will get done! There's a wind; her hair is wild, blown up around her head like feathers.

I've told her I can't stay long. "You can't?" she said. "But we could have tea, I could light a fire … "

"Not today," I said firmly.

He can see her out there, more or less, and he wants her to come back in. He doesn't like it that she's on the other side of the glass. If he lets her slip away, out of his sight, who knows where she might go? She might vanish forever.

I hold his good hand. "She'll come in soon," I say; but *soon* could be a year.

"I want to go home," he says. I know there's no point telling him that home is where he now is, because he means something else. He means the way he was before.

"Where are we now?" I say.

He gives me a crafty look: Am I trying to trip him up? "In a forest," he says. "We need to get back."

"We're all right here," I say.

He considers. "Not much to eat."

"We brought the right supplies," I say.

He is reassured. "But there's not enough wood." He's anxious about this; he says it every day. His feet are cold, he says.

"We can get more wood," I say. "We can cut it."

He's not so sure. "I never thought this would happen," he says. He doesn't mean the stroke, because he doesn't know he's had one. He means getting lost.

"We know what to do," I say. "Anyway, we'll be fine."

"We'll be fine," he says, but he sounds dubious. He doesn't trust me, and he is right. ❿

The story related within this story may be found in its original version in *The Lure of the Labrador Wild*, by Dillon Wallace, published in 1905 by Fleming H. Revell Company and reprinted by Breakwater Books, Newfoundland, in 1977.

Margaret Atwood was born in 1939 in Ottawa, Ontario. She is an internationally acclaimed poet, novelist, story writer, and essayist. "The Labrador Fiasco," published in 1996, incorporates two of her longstanding interests— Canadian history and the Canadian wilderness.

1. *Response*
   a. In a group, discuss the challenges this story presents to the reader. Together, think of strategies that readers could use to overcome the challenges. Present your ideas to the class.
   b. What do you think the *fiasco* is that's referred to in the title?
   c. Describe the narrator's feelings towards the father and towards the explorers. How do you know?
   d. In your view, what does the narrator mean by the last sentence?

2. *Research and Inquiry* One of Margaret Atwood's early works was a book entitled *Survival: A Thematic Guide to Canadian Literature*. Use the Internet and other resources to learn about the main argument Atwood presented in that book and the controversy it caused. What connection do you see between "The Labrador Fiasco" and *Survival*?

3. *Literature Studies* Story Within a Story "The Labrador Fiasco" contains two stories, one nested inside the other. In a group, determine which is the *frame story*—the story that holds the second story. Why do you think Atwood includes the second story? What are the parallels between the two narratives? Design a visual way (a chart, diagram, or poster, for example) of presenting your conclusions.

4. **Critical Thinking** Choose three words that you think best describe nature as it is portrayed in "The Labrador Fiasco." Now choose three words that capture the way nature is portrayed in Judith Currelly's *Travelers*. Give reasons for your interpretations. Which attitude about nature comes closest to your own?

*Travelers,* Judith Currelly. Oil on wood panel.

How do the details of the painting reflect its title and the theme of undertaking a journey?

# *Snow*

By Ann Beattie

*"I know ten ways to move [a story] through time, and my interest is in finding the eleventh. I want to do something that I haven't done before,"* Ann Beattie claims. What conventions of short story writing does Beattie challenge in "Snow"?

I remember the cold night you brought in a pile of logs and a chipmunk jumped off as you lowered your arms. "What do you think *you're* doing in here?" you said, as it ran through the living room. It went through the library and stopped at the front door as though it knew the house well. This would be difficult for anyone to believe, except perhaps as the subject of a poem. Our first week in the house was spent scraping, finding some of the house's secrets, like wallpaper underneath wallpaper. In the kitchen, a pattern of white-gold trellises supported purple grapes as big and round as Ping-Pong balls. When we painted the walls yellow, I thought of the bits of grape that remained underneath and imagined the vine popping through, the way some plants can tenaciously push through anything. The day of the big snow, when you had to shovel the walk and couldn't find your cap and asked me how to wind a towel so that it would stay on your head—you, in the white towel turban, like a crazy king of snow. People liked the idea of our being together, leaving the city for the country. So many people visited, and the fireplace made all of them want to tell amazing stories: the child who happened to be standing on the right corner when the door of the ice cream truck came open and hundreds of Popsicles crashed out; the man standing on the beach, sand sparkling in the sun, one bit glinting more than the rest, stooping to find a diamond ring. Did they talk about amazing things because they thought we'd turn into one of them? Now I think they probably guessed it wouldn't work. It was as hopeless as giving a child a matched cup and saucer. Remember the night, out on the lawn, knee-deep in snow, chins pointed at the sky as the wind whirled down all that whiteness? It seemed that the world had been turned upside down, and we were looking into an enormous field of Queen Anne's lace. Later, headlights off, our car was the first to ride through the newly fallen snow. The world outside the car looked solarized.

You remember it differently. You remember that the cold settled in stages, that a small curve of light was shaved from the moon night after night, until you were no longer surprised the sky was black, that the chipmunk ran to hide in the dark, not simply to a door that led to its escape. Our visitors told the same stories people always tell. One night, giving me a lesson in storytelling, you said, "Any life will seem dramatic if you omit mention of most of it."

This, then, for drama: I drove back to that house not long ago. It was April, and Allen had died. In spite of all the visitors, Allen, next door, had been the good friend in bad times. I sat with his wife in their living room, looking out the glass doors to the backyard, and there was Allen's pool, still covered with black plastic that had been stretched across it for winter. It had rained, and as the rain fell, the cover collected more and more water until it finally spilled onto the concrete. When I left that day, I drove past what had been our house. Three or four crocus were blooming in the front—just a few dots of white, no field of snow. I felt embarrassed for them. They couldn't compete.

This is a story, told the way you say stories should be told: Somebody grew up, fell in love, and spent a winter with her lover in the country. This, of course, is the barest outline, and futile to discuss. It's as pointless as throwing birdseed on the ground while snow still falls fast. Who expects small things to survive when even the largest get lost? People forget years and remember moments. Seconds and symbols are left to sum things up: the black shroud over the pool. Love, in its shortest form, becomes a word. What I remember about all that time is one winter. The snow. Even now, saying "snow," my lips move so that they kiss the air.

No mention has been made of the snowplow that seemed always to be there, scraping snow off our narrow road—an artery cleared, though neither of us could have said where the heart was.

**Ann Beattie** was born in 1947 in Washington, D.C. Her novels and short stories have won her critical acclaim and a wide audience.

*Illinois Farm*, Richard Hamilton Smith.

From what position was this photograph taken? What ideas and emotions has this viewpoint helped the photographer to communicate?

## 1. *Response*

**a.** When you finished the story, did you feel you understood what the author was trying to accomplish? Express your ideas about the author's purpose in two or three statements. Do you have any questions about the work? Write those down, as well.

**b.** In a group, try to answer each other's questions about "Snow."

## 2. *Literature Studies* Short Story Elements

Create a list of the most important elements of a short story (for example, setting, mood). Which elements are strongest in "Snow," and which are weakest? Based on your analysis, would you classify "Snow" as a short story? Why or why not?

## 3. *Writing* Storytelling

Using *free writing* (writing non-stop for about five minutes), explore the implications of the following statement:

> "One night, giving me a lesson in storytelling, you said, 'Any life will seem dramatic if you omit mention of most of it.'"

## 4. *Media* Visual Essay

Create a visual essay from any four consecutive sentences in this story and any combination of magazine illustrations and original artwork. The visuals you choose need not correspond literally to the words. Aim for metaphoric and symbolic correspondences between text and visuals.

*"Much later, I discovered that my father was famous
in the region because of what the people called his 'gift'..."
But it seems that some gifts are impossible to preserve.*

# A Secret Lost
# in the Water

BY ROCH CARRIER

Translated from the French by Sheila Fischman

After I started going to school my father scarcely talked any more.
I was very intoxicated by the new game of spelling; my father had
little skill for it (it was my mother who wrote our letters) and was
convinced I was no longer interested in hearing him tell of his
adventures during the long weeks when he was far away from the
house.

One day, however, he said to me:

"The time's come to show you something."

He asked me to follow him. I walked behind him, not talking,
as we had got in the habit of doing. He stopped in the field before
a clump of leafy bushes.

"Those are called alders," he said.

"I know."

"You have to learn how to choose," my father pointed out.

I didn't understand. He touched each branch of the bush, one
at a time, with religious care.

"You have to choose one that's very fine, a perfect one, like
this."

I looked; it seemed exactly like the others.

My father opened his pocket knife and cut the branch he'd
selected with pious care. He stripped off the leaves and showed me
the branch, which formed a perfect Y.

"You see," he said, "the branch has two arms. Now take one in
each hand. And squeeze them."

I did as he asked and took in each hand one fork of the Y, which
was thinner than a pencil.

"Close your eyes," my father ordered, "and squeeze a little
harder... Don't open your eyes! Do you feel anything?"

"The branch is moving!" I exclaimed, astonished.

Beneath my clenched fingers the alder was wriggling like a
small, frightened snake. My father saw that I was about to drop it.

"Hang on to it!"

"The branch is squirming," I repeated. "And I hear something that sounds like a river!"

"Open your eyes," my father ordered.

I was stunned, as though he'd awakened me while I was dreaming.

"What does it mean?" I asked my father.

"It means that underneath us, right here, there's a little fresh-water spring. If we dig, we could drink from it. I've just taught you how to find a spring. It's something my own father taught me. It isn't something you learn in school. And it isn't useless: a man can get along without writing and arithmetic, but he can never get along without water."

Much later, I discovered that my father was famous in the region because of what the people called his 'gift': before digging a well they always consulted him; they would watch him prospecting the fields or the hills, eyes closed, hands clenched on the fork of an alder bough. Wherever my father stopped, they marked the ground; there they would dig; and from there water would gush forth.

Years passed; I went to other schools, saw other countries, I had children, I wrote some books and my poor father is lying in the earth where so many times he had found fresh water.

One day someone began to make a film about my village and its inhabitants, from whom I've stolen so many of the stories that I tell. With the film crew we went to see a farmer to capture the image of a sad man: his children didn't want to receive the inheritance he'd spent his whole life preparing for them—the finest farm in the area. While the technicians were getting cameras and microphones ready the farmer put his arm around my shoulders, saying:

"I knew your father well."

"Ah! I know. Everybody in the village knows each other … No one feels like an outsider."

"You know what's under your feet?"

"Hell?" I asked, laughing.

"Under your feet there's a well. Before I dug I called in specialists from the Department of Agriculture; they did research, they analyzed shovelfuls of dirt; and they made a report where they said there wasn't any water on my land. With the family, the animals, the crops, I need water. When I saw that those specialists hadn't found any I thought of your father and I asked him to come over. He didn't want to; I think he

> There is creative reading as well as creative writing.
>
> Ralph Waldo Emerson

was pretty fed up with me because I'd asked those specialists instead of him. But finally he came; he went and cut off a little branch, then he walked around for a while with his eyes shut; he stopped, he listened to something we couldn't hear and then he said to me: 'Dig right here, there's enough water to get your whole flock drunk and drown your specialists besides.' We dug and found water. Fine water that's never heard of pollution."

The film people were ready; they called to me to take my place.

"I'm gonna show you something," said the farmer, keeping me back. "You wait right here."

He disappeared into a shack which he must have used to store things, then came back with a branch which he held out to me.

"I never throw nothing away; I kept the alder branch your father cut to find my water. I don't understand, it hasn't dried out."

Moved as I touched the branch, kept out of I don't know what sense of piety—and which really wasn't dry—I had the feeling that my father was watching me over my shoulder; I closed my eyes and, standing above the spring my father had discovered, I waited for the branch to writhe, I hoped the sound of gushing water would rise to my ears.

The alder stayed motionless in my hands and the water beneath the earth refused to sing.

Somewhere along the roads I'd taken since the village of my childhood I had forgotten my father's knowledge.

"Don't feel sorry," said the man, thinking no doubt of his farm and his childhood; "nowadays fathers can't pass on anything to the next generation."

And he took the alder branch from my hands.


French-Canadian writer **Roch Carrier** was born in Québec in 1937. His novels, plays, and short stories are popular with readers and critics alike. "A Secret Lost in the Water" first appeared in Carrier's *The Hockey Sweater and Other Stories* (1979). In 1999, he was appointed to the prestigious position of Canada's National Librarian.

**1. *Response***

**a.** Describe the relationship the narrator has with his father. Use a chart to show how the narrator and his father are similar, but also different.

**b.** What point do you think the author, Roch Carrier, is making about the connections between fathers and sons? Do you agree or disagree with Carrier? Explain.

**c.** Find at least three pieces of evidence to suggest that the narrator regrets that he has lost the secret his father gave him. Now find three details that suggest the narrator is happy with the decision he made about becoming a writer. What do you think Carrier might be saying in his short story?

**d.** Suggest reasons why the first person point of view can help to make a work of fiction read like a true story. Have you ever used that technique in your own writing to make a story seem authentic?

**2. *Oral Language*** *Opening Statement* Prepare an opening statement for a debate on whether or not the son should have been more careful about preserving the secret his father imparted to him. In your statement, you should indicate where your sympathies lie: with the father and the farmer, or with the narrator. Be prepared to present your statement to the class.

**3. *Making Connections*** In a small group, explore the meaning of the term *self-discovery*. In what ways are "Mirror Image" and "A Secret Lost in the Water" both about self-discovery? Discuss whether the two stories have much in common. Create a list of other works (stories, novels, movies, and so on) that deal with self-discovery. Do these works feature similar conflicts or story lines? Explain.

Sometimes a new perspective on life is only an
impulse away...

# The Pose By Anwer Khan

*Translated by Muhammad Umar Memon*

Who knows what got into her head. She abruptly broke her stride
and slipped into Shandar Cloth Store. Then she opened the door of
the show window and, deftly, removing the lovely mannequin,
stood herself in the plastic dummy's place and assumed its pose.

It was evening. The street was packed with people, but they
were so preoccupied as they went their way that none of them
noticed what she had just done.

Why did she do it? She probably didn't know that herself. True,
she was something of a daredevil in her childhood. But now she was
a grown young woman, a college student, smart, sophisticated,
urbane. Even the most daring boys at the college got cold feet
walking with her. What she'd just done, well, it just happened. It
was entirely unpremeditated.

Standing in the show window she felt a strange sense of comfort wash upon her. She was now, after all, a part of this bustling
marketplace. She could also look closely at the place, the whole of
it, standing in just one spot, without having to move. Walking as
one of the crowd or while shopping, she never felt herself a part of
the life around her—the buoyant, strident life, full of vigour and
excitement.

Her tense body gradually became unstrung, and an unpro-
voked smile came to her lips. She quite liked it—standing with one
foot slightly forward, the hem of her sari going over her head and
then dropping down to wrap itself around the joint of her right
elbow. She looked positively ravishing. She could stand in her new
posture forever, she thought, overcome by a sudden impulse,
although her knees had already begun to ache from the pressure.

She was just considering easing up on her heels a little when
her eyes caught sight of a peasant who suddenly cut through the
crowd on the sidewalk and came over to the show window and
began gawking at her with eyes at once full of lust and wonder. His

eyes seemed to say: Incredible! These craftsmen can be so skilful! How they make statues that look like real people!

It was good the glass panel stood between them, otherwise the country bumpkin would certainly have ventured to touch her.

The peasant perhaps wanted to linger on for a while, but the scouring glances of the passersby forced him to move on. As soon as he had moved away, she relaxed her feet a little. Even shook them a bit. But now her lips began to feel dry. "Just a little while longer," she told her lips under her breath, "and then I'll take you to a restaurant and treat you to a glass of ice water, followed by a steaming cup of some finely brewed tea." Her thirst let up a bit and she slipped back into her former pose.

She certainly had no wish to exhibit herself like this to the pedestrians. Perhaps the thought had never even entered her mind. Rather, it pleased her to think that she was now a full participant in the teeming life around her. It was a strange feeling. She had never experienced it before.

"Oh!"—the expression came from the lips of two college girls—"how lifelike!"

Their voices, travelling along the glass panels and filtering through the holes in the steel strips holding the frame, came upon her softly, as if from a great distance.

The two girls gawked at her with admiration as they exchanged a few words among themselves, while she looked at them with tenderness. She was happy. Incredibly happy. No one had looked at her so appreciatively before. At least not in her presence. Like a kind and caring queen receiving the adulation of her subjects, she sustained her regal pose until the girls had once again melted into the crowd and disappeared from view.

"Let's see who comes next?" she thought to herself.

Her feet had again started to protest. This time around, though, she sent them a warning, a rather stern one: Scoundrels, stay put! Can't you wait even a little? She wouldn't care a hoot about their protest, she decided.

She was still congratulating herself on her firmness when she caught sight of a cop who had just separated from the crowd and after taking a pinch of chewing tobacco from a box he held was rubbing it with his thumb. The moment he saw her, his hand stopped dead, his mouth fell open, and his eyes widened. She stared at the cop sweetly. The cop's eyelashes began to flap frantically; he rubbed the tobacco hastily and stuffing it between his lower lip and tooth practically stuck his eyes against the glass of the show window.

She was overcome by a powerful urge to laugh, but managed to stop herself with the greatest difficulty. Suddenly her feet began to itch uncontrollably. There was even a slight, involuntary tremble. But the cop thought it was a mere illusion, or the effect of the tobacco.

The cop stared at her for a long time. He would withdraw a little, then come back and inspect her closely. This went on for so long that she began to tire. Is the idiot going to leave the place at all?—she wondered. She was feeling uncomfortable. She knew she couldn't go on standing in that pose. All the same, she also knew that she was safe inside the show window. Where would she find such protection outside?

Thank God the cop finally decided to leave, and she drew a breath of relief, loosened her hands and feet, straightened up her tense back, indeed even massaged it a bit. Night was approaching and the crowd had thinned down to a few swift-footed pedestrians.

Soon it will grow dark, she thought. She'd better get out of here while there was still some light. The cloth store must be emptying out. Somebody might see her getting out of the show window. She'd have to be very careful ... and fast. And yet there was such comfort inside the show window! How she wallowed in that pleasure! Another ten minutes? Why not ...

She was still mulling over this when she spotted her girlfriend Sheyama on the sidewalk. Right away she sprang into her former pose and held her breath. Sheyama threw an inattentive look in her direction and because her thoughts were elsewhere, the danger, luckily, was averted. The thought that some of her acquaintances might spot her here had not occurred to her until Sheyama came along. This was precisely the time when her older brother returned from work, she recalled with horror. He's already suffering from a heart ailment. What if he saw the family's honour exposed so shamelessly out on the street? Wouldn't he drop dead?

Two boys appeared in her field of vision. They were returning from school, their satchels glued to their backs. They looked with zesty curiosity and pasted their faces—eyes and all—flat against the glass.

"Hey, she's real," the voice of one of the boys entered her ear faintly. Once again she wanted to laugh.

"Punk—it's plastic," the other boy said. "Whoever uses a live model?"

"But she looks so real. Seems she'd open her mouth and start speaking any moment."

"That's because of the evening. In proper light, you'd see."

"Hi!" the boy said as he winked at her mischievously.

The other one broke into a gale of laughter. Then he too waved at her and said "Bye!" and the two walked out of her field of vision.

As soon as they were gone, she suddenly began to laugh, but just as suddenly, became very nervous.

A young man was looking at her with perplexed eyes from across the glass. When their eyes met, he smiled. She smiled back, if only to hide her trepidation. She quickly grabbed the plastic dummy, and tried to install it, pretending to be one of the store attendants.

The youth's eyes were still riveted on her.

Arranging the sari around the mannequin she looked at the youth from the corner of her eye to see who he was looking at. His eyes lingered briefly at the plastic figure, then bounced off it and became glued to her.

She backed up, supremely confident, opened the door to the show window and walked out.

None of the store attendants saw her go out, or if they did, she was so agile and so fast that they couldn't figure out what had happened. The doorman didn't notice as he was busy talking to one of the sales clerks.

Confidently she strode away, briskly but lightly, happy and satisfied. As though she'd just unloaded the entire pestering weight of her body and soul. After she had walked away some distance, she turned around and looked back. The youth was still staring at her, perhaps with wonder.

She quickly turned down another street.

**Anwer Khan,** born in Bombay, India, holds M.A. degrees in Urdu and Persian. Writing since the 1960s, he has published three collections of short stories and a novel. "The Pose" was taken from his collection, *Yad Basere* (1990).

## 1. *Response*

**a.** Though the exact setting of "The Pose" is never mentioned, there are some references within the story that can help readers make an educated guess. Where and when do you think the story might take place? Explain your reasoning.

**b.** What does the protagonist seem to gain from her impulsive decision to pose in the store window? Speculate on why she might have those reactions.

**c.** Suggest reasons why the author chose to have the young woman remain nameless in this story.

**d.** Would you describe yourself as the kind of person who acts impulsively? Do you think this affected the way you responded to "The Pose"? Explain.

## 2. *Writing* *Changing Points of View*
Rewrite the first four paragraphs using the first person point of view. What effect does changing the point of view have on the telling of the story? Which narrative point of view is more effective for this particular story? Explain.

## 3. *Language Conventions* *Adjectives and Adverbs*
Adjectives describe people, places, and things. Adverbs tell us how things are done. These words can suggest to readers how the author or protagonist feels about what is happening. Make a list of all the adjectives and adverbs used to describe the young woman. Next, create a similar list of words used to describe the various people who stare at her in the window. What conclusions can you draw based on these lists? Select a passage of your own writing and evaluate whether you have used adjectives and adverbs effectively.

## 4. *Oral Language* *Role Playing*
If the protagonist later revealed her adventure to Sheyama, what would the two friends say to each other? With a partner, role-play the conversation that might unfold.

> "Blowing up an elephant is not an
> everyday job."

# The Elephant

### By Slawomir Mrozek

*Translated from the Polish by Konrad Syrop*

THE DIRECTOR AT THE ZOOLOGICAL GARDENS HAD SHOWN himself to be an upstart. He regarded his animals simply as stepping stones on the road of his own career. He was indifferent to the educational importance of his establishment. In his zoo the giraffe had a short neck, the badger had no burrow and the whistlers, having lost all interest, whistled rarely and with some reluctance. These shortcomings should not have been allowed, especially as the zoo was often visited by parties of schoolchildren.

The zoo was in a provincial town, and it was short of some of the most important animals, among them the elephant. Three thousand rabbits were a poor substitute for the noble giant. However, as our country developed, the gaps were being filled in a well-planned manner. On the occasion of the anniversary of the liberation, on 22nd July, the zoo was notified that it had at long last been allocated an elephant. All the staff, who were devoted to their work, rejoiced at this news. All the greater was their surprise when they learned that the director had sent a letter to Warsaw, renouncing the allocation and putting forward a plan for obtaining an elephant by more economic means.

"I, and all the staff," he had written, "are fully aware how heavy a burden falls upon the shoulders of Polish miners and foundry men because of the elephant. Desirous of reducing our costs, I suggest that the elephant mentioned in your communication should be replaced by one of our own procurement. We can make an elephant out of rubber, of the correct size, fill it with air and place it behind railings. It will be carefully painted the correct color and even on close inspection will be indistinguishable from the real animal. It is well known that the elephant is a sluggish animal and it does not run and jump about. In the notice on the railings we can state that this particular elephant is particularly sluggish. The money saved in this way can be turned to the purchase of a jet plane or the conservation of some church monument.

"Kindly note that both the idea and its execution are my modest contribution to the common task and struggle.

"I am, etc."

This communication must have reached a soulless official, who regarded his duties in a purely bureaucratic manner and did not examine the heart of the matter but, following only the directive about reduction of expenditure, accepted the director's plan. On hearing the Ministry's approval, the director issued instructions for the making of the rubber elephant.

The carcass was to have been filled with air by two keepers blowing into it from opposite ends. To keep the operation secret the work was to be completed during the night because the people of the town, having heard that an elephant was joining the zoo, were anxious to see it. The director insisted on haste also because he expected a bonus, should his idea turn out to be a success.

The two keepers locked themselves in a shed normally housing a workshop, and began to blow. After two hours of hard blowing they discovered that the rubber skin had risen only a few inches above the floor and its bulge in no way resembled an elephant. The night progressed. Outside, human voices were stilled and only the cry of the jackass interrupted the silence. Exhausted, the keepers stopped blowing and made sure that the air already inside the elephant should not escape. They were not young and were unaccustomed to this kind of work.

"If we go on at this rate," said one of them, "we shan't finish by morning. And what am I to tell my missus? She'll never believe me if I say that I spent the night blowing up an elephant."

"Quite right," agreed the second keeper. "Blowing up an elephant is not an everyday job. And it's all because our director is a leftist."

They resumed their blowing, but after another half-hour they felt too tired to continue. The bulge on the floor was larger but still nothing like the shape of an elephant.

"It's getting harder all the time," said the first keeper.

"It's an uphill job, all right," agreed the second. "Let's have a little rest."

While they were resting, one of them noticed a gas pipe ending in a valve. Could they not fill the elephant with gas? He suggested it to his mate.

They decided to try. They connected the elephant to the gas pipe, turned the valve, and to their joy in a few minutes there was a full sized beast standing in the shed. It looked real: the enormous body, legs like columns, huge ears and the inevitable trunk. Driven by ambition the director had made sure of having in his zoo a very large elephant indeed.

"First class," declared the keeper who had the idea of using gas. "Now we can go home."

In the morning the elephant was moved to a special run in a central position, next to the monkey cage. Placed in front of a large real rock it looked fierce and magnificent. A big notice proclaimed: "Particularly sluggish. Hardly moves."

Among the first visitors that morning was a party of children from the local school. The teacher in charge of them was planning to give them an object-lesson about the elephant. He halted the group in front of the animal and began:

"The elephant is a herbivorous mammal. By means of its trunk it pulls out young trees and eats their leaves."

The children were looking at the elephant with enraptured admiration. They were waiting for it to pull out a young tree, but the beast stood still behind its railings.

"... The elephant is a direct descendant of the now-extinct mammoth. It's not surprising, therefore, that it's the largest living land animal."

The more conscientious pupils were making notes.

"... Only the whale is heavier than the elephant, but then the whale lives in the sea. We can safely say that on land the elephant reigns supreme."

A slight breeze moved the branches of the trees in the zoo.

"... The weight of a fully grown elephant is between nine and thirteen thousand pounds."

At that moment the elephant shuddered and rose in the air. For a few seconds it stayed just above the ground, but a gust of wind blew it upward until its mighty silhouette was against the sky. For a short while people on the ground could see the four circles of its feet, its bulging belly and the trunk, but soon, propelled by the wind, the elephant sailed above the fence and disappeared above the treetops. Astonished monkeys in the cage continued staring into the sky.

They found the elephant in the neighboring botanical gardens.

It had landed on a cactus and punctured its rubber hide.

The schoolchildren who had witnessed the scene in the zoo soon started neglecting their studies and turned into hooligans. It is reported that they drink liquor and break windows. And they no longer believe in elephants.

**Slawomir Mrozek** was born in Borzecin, Poland, in 1930. He studied architecture, oriental culture, and painting, and initially worked as a journalist. His writing established him as one of Poland's best-known playwrights and satirists. In 1968, Mrozek moved to Paris because his work was banned due to its controversial nature. However, by 1970, it was once again performed and published in Poland.

1. *Response*

   **a.** What does the author achieve by including the line, "… only the cry of the jackass interrupted the silence"? Identify some other lines that create a similar effect.

   **b.** Despite its absurdity, the story is quite realistic in a number of ways. What techniques does the author use to create a sense of realism in the telling of the tale?

   **c.** What do you think is the purpose of the last paragraph in the story? What would be lost if it were omitted?

   **d.** In what way might "The Elephant" be considered a *satire* (a work that criticizes something—for example, a person, a characteristic, an institution, or a government—by depicting it in a humorous, sarcastic, or scornful way)?

2. *Literature Studies* Allegory  Read only on the literal level, an **allegory** can seem unrealistic, ridiculous, or trite. On the symbolic level, however, an allegory takes on special significance. What do you think the various elements and characters in "The Elephant" might symbolize? Present your interpretation of the moral lesson it presents.

An **allegory** is a simple story, such as a fable or parable, whose major purpose is to teach a moral lesson. An allegory can always be read on two levels—one literal, the other symbolic.

3. **Making Connections** In a brief comparison, identify the similarities between "The Elephant" and "He-y, Come On Ou-t!" Develop a chart to highlight their similarities and differences.

4. **Language Conventions** *Active and Passive Voice* The second-last sentence in the story is written in the **passive voice**: "It is reported that they drink liquor and break windows." Try to rewrite the sentence in the **active voice.** What difficulty did you encounter? Why do you think that the passive voice is often used in documents created by scientists, historians, and government officials?

In a sentence written in the **active voice**, the subject of the verb *performs* the action. In a sentence written in the **passive voice** the subject of the verb *receives* the action. In some passive constructions, the person or thing that performs the actions is unclear.

# The Cask of Amontillado

By Edgar Allan Poe

The setting of this classic story is a nameless European city in an unspecified year—perhaps sometime during the eighteenth century. The action takes place during carnival, a public festival in which people wore elaborate costumes and participated in wild celebrations.

The thousand injuries of Fortunato I had borne as I best could, but when he ventured upon insult I vowed revenge. You, who so well know the nature of my soul, will not suppose, however, that I gave utterance to a threat. *At length* I would be avenged; this was a point definitely settled—but the very definitiveness with which it was resolved precluded the idea of risk. I must not only punish but punish with impunity. A wrong is unredressed when retribution overtakes its redresser. It is equally unredressed when the avenger fails to make himself felt as such to him who has done the wrong.

It must be understood that neither by word nor deed had I given Fortunato cause to doubt my good will. I continued, as was my wont, to smile in his face, and he did not perceive that my smile *now* was at the thought of his immolation.

He had a weak point—this Fortunato—although in other regards he was a man to be respected and even feared. He prided himself on his connoisseurship in wine. Few Italians have the true virtuoso spirit. For the most part their enthusiasm is adopted to suit the time and opportunity, to practise imposture upon the British and Austrian *millionaires*. In painting and gemmary,[1] Fortunato, like his countrymen, was a quack, but in the matter of old wines he was sincere. In this respect I did not differ from him materially;—I was skilful in the Italian vintages myself, and bought largely whenever I could.

---

[1] **gemmary:** gems, jewels

It was about dusk, one evening during the supreme madness of the carnival season, that I encountered my friend. He accosted me with excessive warmth, for he had been drinking much. The man wore motley. He had on a tight-fitting parti-striped dress, and his head was surmounted by the conical cap and bells. I was so pleased to see him that I thought I should never have done wringing his hand.

I said to him—"My dear Fortunato, you are luckily met. How remarkably well you are looking to-day. But I have received a pipe[2] of what passes for Amontillado,[3] and I have my doubts."

"How?" said he. "Amontillado? A pipe? Impossible! And in the middle of the carnival!"

"I have my doubts," I replied; "and I was silly enough to pay the full Amontillado price without consulting you in the matter. You were not to be found, and I was fearful of losing a bargain."

"Amontillado!"

"I have my doubts."

"Amontillado!"

"And I must satisfy them."

"Amontillado!"

"As you are engaged, I am on my way to Luchresi. If any one has a critical turn, it is he. He will tell me—"

"Luchresi cannot tell Amontillado from Sherry."

"And yet some fools will have it that his taste is a match for your own."

"Come, let us go."

"Whither?"

"To your vaults."

"My friend, no; I will not impose upon your good nature. I perceive you have an engagement. Luchresi—"

"I have no engagement;—come."

"My friend, no. It is not the engagement, but the severe cold with which I perceive you are afflicted. The vaults are insufferably damp. They are encrusted with nitre."

"Let us go, nevertheless. The cold is merely nothing. Amontillado! You have been imposed upon. And as for Luchresi, he cannot distinguish Sherry from Amontillado."

Thus speaking, Fortunato possessed himself of my arm; and putting on a mask of black silk and drawing a *roquelaire*[4] closely about my person, I suffered him to hurry me to my palazzo.

---

[2]**pipe:** a very large cask of wine   [3]**Amontillado:** a particularly rare and valuable sherry wine
[4]***roquelaire:*** a knee-length cloak

There were no attendants at home; they had absconded to make merry in honour of the time. I had told them that I should not return until the morning, and had given them explicit orders not to stir from the house. These orders were sufficient, I well knew, to insure their immediate disappearance, one and all, as soon as my back was turned.

I took from their sconces two flambeaux, and giving one to Fortunato, bowed him through several suites of rooms to the archway that led into the vaults. I passed down a long and winding staircase, requesting him to be cautious as he followed. We came at length to the foot of the descent, and stood together on the damp ground of the catacombs of the Montresors.

The gait of my friend was unsteady, and the bells upon his cap jingled as he strode.

"The pipe?" said he.

"It is farther on," said I; "but observe the white web-work which gleams from these cavern walls."

He turned towards me, and looked into my eyes with two filmy orbs that distilled the rheum of intoxication.

"Nitre?" he asked, at length.

"Nitre," I replied. "How long have you had that cough?"

"Ugh! ugh! ugh!—ugh! ugh! ugh!—ugh! ugh! ugh! ugh! ugh! ugh! —ugh! ugh! ugh!"

My poor friend found it impossible to reply for many minutes.

"It is nothing," he said, at last.

"Come," I said, with decision, "we will go back; your health is precious. You are rich, respected, admired, beloved; you are happy, as once I was. You are a man to be missed. For me it is no matter. We will go back; you will be ill, and I cannot be responsible. Besides, there is Luchresi—"

"Enough," he said; "the cough is a mere nothing; it will not kill me. I shall not die of a cough."

"True—true," I replied; "and, indeed, I had no intention of alarming you unnecessarily—but you should use all proper caution. A draught of this Medoc will defend us from the damps."

Here I knocked off the neck of a bottle which I drew from a long row of its fellows that lay upon the mould.

"Drink," I said, presenting him the wine.

He raised it to his lips with a leer. He paused and nodded to me familiarly, while his bells jingled.

"I drink," he said, "to the buried that repose around us."

"And I to your long life."

He again took my arm, and we proceeded.

"These vaults," he said, "are extensive."

"The Montresors," I replied, "were a great and numerous family."

"I forget your arms."[5]

"A huge human foot d'or, in a field azure; the foot crushes a serpent rampant whose fangs are imbedded in the heel."

"And the motto?"

"*Nemo me impune lacessit.*"[6]

"Good!" he said.

The wine sparkled in his eyes and the bells jingled. My own fancy grew warm with the Medoc. We had passed through long walls of piled skeletons, with casks and puncheons intermingling, into the inmost recesses of the catacombs. I paused again, and this time I made bold to seize Fortunato by an arm above the elbow.

"The nitre!" I said; "see, it increases. It hangs like moss upon the vaults. We are below the river's bed. The drops of moisture trickle among the bones. Come, we will go back ere it is too late. Your cough—"

"It is nothing," he said; "let us go on. But first, another draught of the Medoc."

I broke and reached him a flagon of De Grâve. He emptied it at a breath. His eyes flashed with a fierce light. He laughed and threw the bottle upward with a gesticulation I did not understand.

I looked at him in surprise. He repeated the movement—a grotesque one.

"You do not comprehend?" he said.

"Not I," I replied.

"Then you are not of the brotherhood."

"How?"

"You are not of the masons."[7]

"Yes, yes," I said; "yes, yes."

"You? Impossible! A mason?"

"A mason," I replied.

"A sign," he said, "a sign."

"It is this," I answered, producing from beneath the folds of my *roquelaire* a trowel.

"You jest," he exclaimed, recoiling a few paces. "But let us proceed to the Amontillado."

"Be it so," I said, replacing the tool beneath the cloak and again offering him my arm. He leaned upon it heavily. We continued our

---

[5]**arms:** coat of arms

[6]**"*Nemo me impune lacessit.*":** "No one attacks me with *impunity.*" (without being punished)

[7]**masons:** Freemasons, an organization of men; once a secret society with its own signs and rituals

route in search of the Amontillado. We passed through a range of low arches, descended, passed on, and descending again, arrived at a deep crypt, in which the foulness of the air caused our flambeaux rather to glow than flame.

At the most remote end of the crypt there appeared another less spacious. Its walls had been lined with human remains, piled to the vault overhead, in the fashion of the great catacombs of Paris. Three sides of this interior crypt were still ornamented in this manner. From the fourth the bones had been thrown down, and lay promiscuously upon the earth, forming at one point a mound of some size. Within the wall thus exposed by the displacing of the bones, we perceived a still interior crypt or recess, in depth about four feet, in width three, in height six or seven. It seemed to have been constructed for no especial use within itself, but formed merely the interval between two of the colossal supports of the roof of the catacombs, and was backed by one of their circumscribing walls of solid granite.

It was in vain that Fortunato, uplifting his dull torch, endeavoured to pry into the depth of the recess. Its termination the feeble light did not enable us to see.

"Proceed," I said; "herein is the Amontillado. As for Luchresi—"

"He is an ignoramus," interrupted my friend, as he stepped unsteadily forward, while I followed immediately at his heels. In an instant he had reached the extremity of the niche, and finding his progress arrested by the rock, stood stupidly bewildered. A moment more and I had fettered him to the granite. In its surface were two iron staples, distant from each other about two feet, horizontally. From one of these depended a short chain, from the other a padlock. Throwing the links about his waist, it was but the work of a few seconds to secure it. He was too much astounded to resist. Withdrawing the key I stepped back from the recess.

"Pass your hand," I said, "over the wall; you cannot help feeling the nitre. Indeed it is *very* damp. Once more let me *implore* you to return. No? Then I must positively leave you. But I must first render you all the little attentions in my power."

"The Amontillado!" ejaculated my friend, not yet recovered from his astonishment.

"True," I replied; "the Amontillado."

As I said these words I busied myself among the pile of bones of which I have before spoken. Throwing them aside, I soon uncovered a quantity of building stone and mortar. With these materials and with the aid of my trowel, I began vigorously to wall up the entrance of the niche.

I had scarcely laid the first tier of the masonry when I discovered that the intoxication of Fortunato had in a great measure worn off. The earliest indication I had of this was a low moaning cry from the depth of the recess. It was *not* the cry of a drunken man. There was then a long and obstinate silence. I laid the second tier, and the third, and the fourth; and then I heard the furious vibrations of the chain. The noise lasted for several minutes, during which, that I might hearken to it with the more satisfaction, I ceased my labours and sat down upon the bones. When at last the clanking subsided, I resumed the trowel, and finished without interruption the fifth, the sixth, and the seventh tier. The wall was now nearly upon a level with my breast. I again paused, and holding the flambeaux over the mason-work, threw a few feeble rays upon the figure within.

A succession of loud and shrill screams, bursting suddenly from the throat of the chained form, seemed to thrust me violently back. For a brief moment I hesitated, I trembled. Unsheathing my rapier, I began to grope with it about the recess; but the thought of an instant reassured me. I placed my hand upon the solid fabric of the catacombs, and felt satisfied. I reapproached the wall. I replied to the yells of him who clamoured. I re-echoed, I aided, I surpassed them in volume and in strength. I did this, and the clamourer grew still.

It was now midnight, and my task was drawing to a close. I had completed the eighth, the ninth, and the tenth tier. I had finished a portion of the last and the eleventh; there remained but a single stone to be fitted and plastered in. I struggled with its weight; I placed it partially in its destined position. But now there came from out the niche a low laugh that erected the hairs upon my head. It was succeeded by a sad voice, which I had difficulty in recognizing as that of the noble Fortunato. The voice said—

"Ha! ha! ha!—he! he! he!—a very good joke, indeed—an excellent jest. We will have many a rich laugh about it at the palazzo—he! he! he!—over our wine—he! he! he!"

"The Amontillado!" I said.

"He! he! he!—he! he! he!—yes, the Amontillado. But is it not getting late? Will not they be awaiting us at the palazzo, the Lady Fortunato and the rest? Let us be gone."

"Yes," I said, "let us be gone."

*"For the love of God, Montresor!"*

"Yes," I said, "for the love of God!"

But to these words I hearkened in vain for a reply. I grew impatient. I called aloud—

"Fortunato!"

No answer. I called again—

"Fortunato!"

No answer still. I thrust a torch through the remaining aperture and let it fall within. There came forth in return only a jingling of the bells. My heart grew sick; it was the dampness of the catacombs that made it so. I hastened to make an end of my labour. I forced the last stone into its position; I plastered it up. Against the new masonry I re-erected the old rampart of bones. For the half of a century no mortal has disturbed them. *In pace requiescat!*[8]

---

[8] ***In pace requiescat!:*** Rest in peace!

Reproduction of original painting from John Hancock Mutual Life Insurance Company's art exhibit "Faces of Freedom."

**This portrait of Edgar Allan Poe incorporates details from his most famous works, including "The Raven" and "The Tell-Tale Heart."**

**Edgar Allan Poe** (1809–1849) is often referred to as the "father of the short story." Although he did not invent the form, Poe was among the first to define what a short story is and what it should do. According to Poe, "unity of effect or impression" is of utmost importance—all elements of a story, such as character, plot, setting, and mood, should work together to achieve one preconceived effect. Even the first sentence must aim at the purpose of the story. "The Cask of Amontillado" was published in 1841.

**1. *Response***

**a.** Edgar Allan Poe believed that the first sentence of a story should communicate the effect that the author is trying to create. Does Poe achieve that aim in this story? Explain.

**b.** Describe the preparations and precautions Montresor undertook to achieve his goal. What do these tell us about Montresor's character?

**c.** According to Montresor, what is necessary for the perfect revenge? By this standard, is Montresor's revenge perfect?

**d.** An *unreliable narrator* is a narrator whose perspective is obviously biassed and whose views cannot be trusted by the reader. What elements of Montresor's story would you challenge? Explain why.

**2. *Literature Studies*** *Irony* Even though this story is about revenge and murder, there is a strong element of ironic humour. In a small group, find as many examples of **irony** as you can and categorize them as *verbal* (arising from what the characters say) or *situational* (arising from what the characters do). Which of the examples do you find the most ironic?

**Irony** is a method of expression in which the intended meaning is the opposite of, or is different from, the expressed meaning.

3. *Critical Thinking*   Some works are written to enhance our understanding of human nature and the human condition. Other works are created mainly to entertain us, through the use of humour, horror, or suspense, for example. What do you think is the purpose of "The Cask of Amontillado"—to entertain or to comment significantly on life? Use examples from the story to support your viewpoint.

4. *Making Connections*   What do "The Cask of Amontillado" and the story told by the bachelor in Saki's "The Storyteller" have in common? Would the aunt in "The Storyteller" consider Poe's story to be proper or improper? Why?

# Brooms for Sale

By Thomas Raddall

**"Greta's next step could be fatal, but standing still meant certain death."**

This is a true story which happened many years ago. Greta was a young widow then, with a boy aged nine. They lived on a small farm in the woods west of the La Have River, near the coast of Nova Scotia. They were very poor.

Greta did all the farm work herself, tending the cattle, ploughing, seeding, and harvesting. In winter she got her own firewood with an axe in the woods. She was a tall Nova Scotia girl with the heart of a man. She had not the strength of a man, though, and no men lived near enough to help her. That was why the house and barn needed repair, and the fences were falling down. That was why each year the crops were smaller. But Greta would not give up.

One winter she thought of a way to get some extra money. There was a fishing village towards the mouth of the La Have, not many miles away. When the fishermen fitted out their vessels each spring, they needed all sorts of things. One thing was a supply of good brooms—but not the kind you buy in the shops. Fishermen must have a very stiff and strong broom, to sweep the deck after cutting and cleaning the day's catch.

Greta had grown up in a shore village and had seen such things made. You take a stick of birch wood about four feet long and three or four inches thick. Then you take a good sharp jack-knife. First, you must remove the birch bark. Then you start at one end of the stick, cutting a splint or shaving about half an inch wide and about as thick as the knife blade. You keep pushing the knife blade to within eight inches of the other end. There you stop. You go back and start another splint. You keep doing that, round and round the stick, until it is no more than an inch and a half thick. And there is your broom handle.

Now you take the bush of splints hanging near the other end, and bend them back over the eight inches of solid wood remaining there. You bind them together tightly in that position with strong cod-line, and with an axe you cut them off at about twelve inches below the cord. And there is your broom, all in one piece.

The Bank Fleet was very large in those days, and in the course of a season each vessel used a number of brooms. So each winter the outfitters bought a good supply.

Greta decided to make some brooms. The days were short and there were many chores to do in the house and barn, not to mention the wood-pile. She would have to do this extra chore after dark. The whittling made such a mess in her clean kitchen that she took part of the barn for a workshop.

Every evening after supper, when the little boy was asleep, she went to the barn, lit a fire in a rusty tin stove, and sat there hour after hour cutting splints by the light of a lantern. Her hands were used to hard work but after a time the grip on the knife made them sore. She tried wearing gloves, but that was awkward. So she tied a strip of linen over the blisters and went on. What pain she suffered, you can guess. But at last her palms were rough and hard, and she could work without a bandage. Some-times she made four or five brooms before midnight.

By the end of January she had two hundred and forty brooms. It was time to sell them.

One chilly morning in February, she hitched the mare Judy to the sleigh, loaded her brooms, helped her child into the seat, and started for West La Have. She left the little boy in the care of her nearest neighbours, three miles down the road. It was pleasant driving through the woods, with the runners creaking on the snow and the harness bells ringing.

The village appeared, with its wharves and stores, and the wide frozen surface of the river. Greta got out of the sleigh happily. But in the first store she had disappointing news. The ship outfitters at West La Have had a full stock of brooms. They could buy no more.

"You might sell them down the river at East La Have," a store-keeper said, pointing over the ice. Greta looked. In the clear winter air the river did not seem very wide—half a mile, say. And three miles down the east shore was a chance to sell her precious brooms.

"The ice is good," the man said. "Several teams have been across to-day."

So Greta headed the mare across the river. It was pretty, she said afterwards—ice on the broad stream as far as you could see; the white banks and the dark woods; and blue smoke rising in small wisps from the houses by the shore.

When she reached East La Have she was stiff from her long drive in the cold, but she entered the store with a quick step and an eager face. The store-keeper looked out at her load and shook his head.

"Sorry, lady, but it seems everybody's been making brooms this winter. We've got too many now."

Half a dozen fishing captains sat by the stove, smoking and talking over the coming season on the Banks. They looked at the woman from up the river. Her coat was cheap and old, too thin for this sort of weather. They saw the worn overshoes, the home-knit woollen cap, the hands twisting anxiously inside the grey mittens. They looked at her tight mouth, and her eyes holding back the tears.

One of them said quietly, "Buy her brooms. If you don't, we will." The store-keeper called one of his clerks to carry the brooms inside. They made a great heap on the floor.

"Let's see, now. Two hundred and forty brooms at twenty-five cents ..."

"Forty cents," the fishing captain said. "Those are good brooms. I'd say you made them yourself, didn't you, ma'am?"

"Yes," Greta said.

The store-keeper counted out ninety-six dollars—nine tens, a five, and a one. Greta thanked him and the captains in a small, choked voice. As she went out the door one of them said, "You'd better drive home smart, ma'am. Looks like snow." She noticed then that the sunshine was gone, the sky was filled with a grey scud coming in very fast from the sea. A bleak, uneasy wind was blowing this way and that.

Greta had no purse. She stopped and fastened the bank notes to the inside hem of her skirt, using a big safety pin. She drove off, humming a tune to herself, and thinking of the things she could buy now for her boy and for the farm. Before she had gone far, the snow began to fly in small hard specks. When she reached the crossing place, a blizzard was blowing. She could not see across the river.

She turned off the road onto the ice, following the faint tracks of the other teams. After ten minutes the old tracks disappeared, buried in the new snow sweeping along the ice. She had to trust the horse to find the way. Greta was not afraid. After all, it was only half a mile or so.

The snow was now so thick that she could not see past Judy's ears. She let the reins go slack and crouched down in the seat, trying to find a little comfort in the storm. There was none. The snow whirled and stung; it seemed to come from every side. Sometimes it stopped her breath, like a cold white cloth laid over her mouth and nose. The little mare kept plunging her head and snorting in the blasts.

The way seemed strangely long. Greta noticed that the light was growing dim. The afternoon had gone. Soon now, surely, she must see the west shore looming through the storm. The horse went on and on, slipping here and there on patches of bare ice.

At last Judy came to a stop. Greta peered into the swirling snow and saw a dim, pale shape ahead. She shielded her eyes with her mittened hand for a better look. Through the snow-gusts she could see the thing was large, with three slim objects standing upon it and reaching up into the murk. Trees, of course! She cried thankfully, "Good girl, Judy! There's the shore. I knew you'd find it!"

She urged the horse on with a jerk at the reins. Judy went on a few steps and stopped again. The object stretched right across her path. It was close and clear now, and Greta gasped. Her very heart seemed to stop beating. For there, like a ghost risen out of the ice, lay a ship. A ship, of all things! A big schooner with three tall masts, all crusted with snow. What was it doing there? Slowly her mind filled with an awful suspicion. She tried to put it aside, but it came back. At last she faced the truth.

The little mare had been lost all this time. Instead of crossing the ice, they had been wandering down the river, towards the open sea. They were now somewhere near the mouth, where the ice was never safe. To prove it, here was the big three-master, frozen in where the crew had left it moored for the winter.

Poor Greta's heart was beating again in slow hard thumps. She was frightened. She did not know which way to turn. Were vessels anchored with their bows upstream or down? Or were they just moored any way at all? She could not remember.

It was quite dark now. Greta's arms and legs felt numb. One thing was certain, she was freezing there in the bitter wind and snow. So was the little horse. They must move or perish. Greta made up her mind. She got down and took hold of Judy's bridle, turned the sleigh carefully, and began to walk, leading the horse straight away from the long, pointing bow-sprit of the schooner.

The strongest blasts of the storm seemed to come from the right. Greta kept the wind on her right cheek. In that way at least she would avoid moving in a circle.

"Suppose the wind changes?" asked a small cold voice inside her. But that was the voice of fear, and she refused to listen.

The effort of walking took some of the cold ache out of her legs, but there was no feeling in her hands and feet, and her cheeks felt like wood. She kept changing her hold on Judy's bridle and rubbing her face with the other hand. The storm tore at her long full skirt and darted icy fingers through her thin coat. The world seemed full of snow, driving in a sharp slant on the wind, and sweeping along the ice with a hiss like escaping steam.

The mare was not shod for this sort of footing. She slipped and stumbled and seemed very tired. And Greta herself felt weary and empty. She had eaten nothing since the hasty breakfast at the farm.

Sometimes the wind lulled, and the cloud of fine snow drifted slowly about them. Its touch then was soft upon the cheek. Greta was tempted to let Judy go, to lie down on the ice and let that cold white powder go on brushing her face and soothing her fears and worries. Somehow the snow made her think of bed-sheets, clean and cool to the skin. How nice it would be, just to lie down and sleep away the night!

But whenever Greta's eyes closed, and the strength seemed to flow out of her limbs, there came into her mind a picture of the lonely boy at the neighbours' house, with his nose against the glass. She opened her eyes then, and stepped forward strongly in the darkness.

As the night went on, this happened many times. Greta became more and more drowsy with the cold, and more weary, and the little horse lagged and stumbled worse and worse. Finally, after one of those dreamy pauses, as Greta began to lead the horse again, she came upon a black patch in the ice ahead. It extended to the right and left as far as she could see. She moved closer—and stepped back in alarm. It was water—open water. She could hear it lapping against the edge of the ice.

She thought, "This is the end. We have come to the sea."

She closed her eyes, praying slowly and silently. She stood there a long time. At last she put her chin up. Aloud she said, "Judy, it's all or nothing now. Suppose it isn't the sea—suppose it's just the flooded ice along the shore! You know, where the ice sinks and buckles when the tide falls down the river. There's only one way to prove it, Judy. I must go to the edge and let my feet down into the water. Come, girl! Steady now! Come!"

Greta led the mare to the edge of the ice. The water looked very black. The snow was blowing harder than ever.

"If only I could see," she thought, "just for a minute. Just for a second. If only I could be sure." But there was only one way to be sure in this stormy blackness. She took a turn of the reins about her wrist, stooped, and lowered her left foot into the water. It came to her ankle, to her knee. The cold grip of the water sent a pain to her very bones. She gasped and lost her balance.

For one wild moment Greta thought she was gone. The sea! She was plunging into the sea! But her feet came upon something now, something slippery but solid. It was the sunken ice. She was standing over her knees in water. She paused to gather courage and her breath. She waded out to the length of the reins. The flooded ice held firm. It was tilted against hidden rocks, and now the water barely reached her trembling knees.

"Come, Judy," she cried, and pulled on the reins. The mare snorted and would not move. Greta threw her whole weight on the reins. Judy tried to draw back, but her worn iron shoes had no grip on the ice. Snorting with fear, she was dragged over the edge into the water. Greta found herself being dragged by the reins about her hand. The horse had floundered past her. She caught hold on the lurching sleigh. Dimly she saw a solid whiteness looming out of the windy dark. It was the shore—a pasture deep in snow.

Greta took the mare's head and led her up the bank. There was a low fence. The poles were rotten and she broke them down. She led Judy along inside the fence, wading through the drifts until she came to a gate and saw a light. Then she was standing at Judy's head outside a house and crying for help.

A man and a woman came to the door. She cried again, and they ran out to her. The man unhitched Judy quickly and took her off to the warmth and shelter of his barn. The woman half-led, half-carried Greta into her kitchen. Greta's clothes were crusted with snow, her wet skirts frozen stiff. But before she would let the good woman do anything for her, she stooped and turned up the icy hem of her skirt.

The precious packet was still there. She counted the notes with her numb white fingers. She laughed shakily. It was all there, the money she had made with her own hands, the money she had saved by her own courage in the storm.

**Thomas Head Raddall** (1913–1994) was an essayist, a short story writer and, most notably, an historical novelist. Much of his work was inspired by the stories and people of Nova Scotia, where he lived for most of his life.

## 1. *Response*

**a.** Describe in detail someone who takes action and fights the odds; either someone you know or someone you have read about or seen in a film. Why do we enjoy reading or hearing about such people?

**b.** Even though "Brooms for Sale" is a work of fiction, we are told in the opening sentence that it is "a true story which happened many years ago." Why do you think Thomas Raddall started his story with that statement? What does he gain and what does he lose as a result?

2. **Literature Studies** *Conflict*  Conflict is an important element of most narratives; however, conflict does not always involve two or more characters who oppose one another. Identify the main conflict or conflicts in "Brooms for Sale." What other kinds of conflict have you encountered in narratives you have read or viewed?

3. **Media** *Real-life Heroes*  People love true stories about individuals whose bravery and determination enable them to overcome great obstacles. Find an example of such a story from one of the popular media (TV, newspaper, magazine, or film). Write a brief summary that tells about the real-life hero and the challenge he or she faced. Did this story have any personal significance for you? Explain.

4. **Making Connections**  In what ways are Greta and Walter Mitty ("The Secret Life of Walter Mitty") similar and different? Include examples from both stories in your comparison.

# The Liberation of Rome

Today, a *vandal* is someone who commits an act of intentional destruction. But who were the first Vandals?

By Robin Hemley

A young woman named Amy Buleric sat in my office looking down at her feet. I figured someone had died, or maybe she was having emotional problems, or was sick. I bolstered myself for whatever horror or misfortune she might throw my way. A colleague of mine forces students to bring in obituaries when they claim a relative has died, but I think that's pathetic. I'd rather believe a student and risk being a fool than become power-crazed. So I was bolstering myself because I was afraid to hear what Amy Buleric was going to tell me about the reason for her absence for the last three weeks.

One time a student sent me a note, "Dr. Radlisch, I'm sorry I can't finish the paper on Hannibal for you." The next day I learned the boy had killed himself—not because of my paper, of course. He had problems I only found out about later. He must have sent me that note out of a pitiful sense of duty. Still, his words haunt me even today.

This young woman was fidgety, not looking at me, and so I sat there patiently, waiting for her to find the courage to tell me whatever it was that bothered her.

"Dr. Radlisch," she said finally, her voice almost a whisper.

"Take your time, Amy," I said, just as softly.

She looked past me to one of my bookshelves. "Why do you have that sign in your office?"

I sat up and turned around so quickly that a muscle popped in my neck. The sign was hand-lettered, done by a friend of my daughter, Claudia, who specializes in calligraphy for weddings. It reads, "If Rome be weak, where shall strength be found?"

"It's a quote from the poet Lucan," I said.

"Yes, I know," she said, a bangled arm sweeping aside her hair. She looked at me with what seemed suddenly like defiance and contempt. "But why is it here? It's . . . like . . . propaganda."

"I'm not sure I understand what you're saying, Amy," I said. I sat back in my chair. My thoughts, my voice became formal. "I thought we were here to discuss your absences, any problems you've been having."

I saw she was about to cry, so I stopped. "I mean," I said, softening my voice, "it's hard to find a solution unless I know what's wrong. Still, I'm glad you stopped in here to talk. I hate it when students simply disappear without a word."

It was too late. She started to cry, and I could see this was the last thing she wanted to do, that she was terribly embarrassed. The tears ran down her face and she didn't make any move to wipe them away.

"I wanted to disappear," she said, "but I couldn't. I had to confront you. That sign is my problem. Part of it anyway."

"Confront me?" I said. I scooted my chair back an inch or two.

"You've probably never had someone like me in one of your classes, and so there was no one to challenge your ideas."

"Ms. Buleric," I said. "I teach Roman history. I don't know what you're talking about. I have no ideas to be challenged. I voice the ideas of the ancients with my tongue, their accounts. I'm not sure where this is all leading, but I thought we were here to talk about your absences."

"I am here to talk about your lies," she said.

I stood up. Amy Buleric didn't rise from her chair and leave as I expected she would. Here I'd thought she needed my sympathy, my help, and she'd only come to accuse me of telling lies.

I sat on the edge of my desk and folded my arms. "How old are you, Amy? Nineteen. Twenty?"

"Twenty," she said.

"Why are you here?" I asked.

"Someone needs to stop you from telling lies."

I waved my hand at her. "Not that. I mean, why are you in college?" I smiled to show I wasn't her enemy. "Do you feel that you know everything already? Or do you think that college might just possibly, just on an outside chance, teach you something—something that might even challenge some of your old notions or the notions of your parents?"

> Storytelling reveals meaning without committing the error of defining it.
> Hannah Arendt

"What about you, Dr. Radlisch?" she said, sitting up straight in her chair. "Do you know everything already? What about your old notions? Can they be challenged?"

"People say I'm open-minded," I said, glancing at my watch.

"I'm here to better my people," she said, looking around the office as though her people had gathered around her.

"Your people? Are you a Mormon?"

"No."

"You're not . . . I mean, you don't look . . ."

"I'm a Vandal, Dr. Radlisch."

I put my chin in my hand. "A Vandal," was all I could manage to say.

"Part Vandal," she said. "Over half."

"You deface property?" I said.

"Another lie," she said. "Another stinking Roman lie." She spat on my carpet.

"You spat on my carpet," I told her and pointed to it.

"I'm a Vandal, Dr. Radlisch," she said. "If you only knew the truth about us."

"Amy," I said calmly. "I'm not doubting you, of course. But what you're telling me is that you're a Vandal. V-A-N-D-A-L. Vandal. Like the tribe? The one that disappeared from history in the sixth century A.D. when Belisarius defeated them and sold them into slavery?"

"Pig," she said. "Dog. Roman dung. Belisarius." And she spat again.

"Please stop spitting on my carpet," I asked her.

She nodded and folded her arms primly in her lap.

"And you're here in my office to set the record straight," I said.

"There isn't any record, Dr. Radlisch," she said. "That's the point. The Vandal tradition is entirely oral. We don't trust the written word. That was the way of the Romans. 'Lies are the province of Romans and writers.' That's an old Vandal proverb. The only record you have is the record of the Romans. They tell you that we were a war-like people who invaded Gaul at the beginning of the fifth century. But that was only because the Huns attacked us first. They drove us out of the Baltic. And we didn't attack the Gauls. We were just defending ourselves! Then the Franks defeated us in 409 and we fled into Spain. We were only there twenty years when a lying Roman governor invited us into North Africa to establish an independent homeland on the ashes of Carthage. We should have known better than to set up camp in Carthage. The only reason we captured Rome was to stop their oppression of us and other peoples who they had colonized or destroyed.

We didn't sack Rome. We liberated it."

She knew her history. Or at least a version, one that I had never heard before.

"And now you're coming forward."

"We've always been here," she said. "You've never noticed."

I wanted to believe her, but I was having a little difficulty. "So for the last fourteen hundred years . . ."

"That's right," she said. "Oh, we've intermarried some, but we've kept our traditions alive." She started to wail. Her eyes were closed and her mouth was stretched in an unnatural grimace. After a minute of this, she stopped, opened her eyes, and wiped her brow.

"Birth song," she announced.

"It's very different," I said. "Haunting."

She seemed pleased that I'd said this. She bowed her head. "For over a millennium our voices have been silenced. No one wanted to hear the Vandal songs. No one cared, though I suppose we were lucky. In some ways, we prefer the world's indifference to its attention. As soon as you're recognized, you're hunted and destroyed. So we waited. And now we're back."

My shoulders tensed and I rubbed my neck where the muscle had popped.

"Thank you for coming forward," I told her. "I know how hard it must be for you. I'm sure there are many things you could teach me."

She smiled at me again and all the anger seemed to be gone. "About the paper that's due?" she said.

"What?"

"Lies are the province of Romans and writers."

At first I didn't get it, but then I saw what she was telling me. "Oh, right," I said. "I guess you can't write it, can you?"

"No, I'm sorry," she said.

"No, don't be sorry," I said, reaching over and nearly touching her shoulder, but not quite. "I understand. I understand completely. It's part of your tradition."

"The Vandal tradition," she said. "Thanks, Dr. Radlisch. I knew you'd understand."

"That's my middle name."

"It is?"

"No, Amy. It's just a turn-of-phrase."

"Oh," she said, and she smiled. She liked me now. I could tell.

But I felt saddened. I was so used to teaching my subject a certain way. I had found a strange comfort in Lucan's quote, but now his question seemed unanswerable, at least by me. "Where shall strength be found?" How was I going to learn the new ways?

That night, I dreamed about my student who had killed himself. He was accusing me of something. He told me I was going to flunk out. I panicked and shot him. That was the dream. Ludicrous, but when I awoke, it felt so real that I nearly cried with relief. When I went to my office that day, I almost expected to see graffiti scrawled on the walls, "Death to All Vandals." But there was none. The walls were clean. No one had defaced them. What's more, Amy never showed up in class again. On the final transcript beside her name there was simply a blank, no "Withdrawn" as I'd hoped. It was up to me. I didn't know what to do. I couldn't give her an "A." But I couldn't flunk her. She knew her history. So I settled on a "B." But why had she stopped coming to class? Was it me? I thought we understood one another now. As I always told my students, they should come see me, no matter what the problem, before they just disappear.

American author **Robin Hemley** publishes both fiction and non-fiction. His short stories have won numerous awards. He teaches creative writing at Western Washington University in Bellingham, Washington.

## 1. *Response*

**a.** When you first read the title of this story, what did you think it might be about? Now that you've completed the story, do you think the title is well chosen? Explain.

**b.** Imagine you are Amy Buleric. Instead of visiting Dr. Radlisch, you decide to give him a brief written note explaining why you can't complete the paper he has assigned. What does your note say?

**c.** Is Amy just a student who has invented a very clever excuse, or is she really a Vandal? And does the professor believe her story, or is he still a smug Roman "sympathizer" at the end? Did the conflict between them end decisively? Give reasons for your point of view.

2. **Oral Language** *Explore Ideas* In a group, discuss the following four quotations, drawing on your knowledge of history. To what extent do you agree with them? What are the implications of these statements? Present your conclusions to the class.

> "Those who cannot remember the past are condemned to repeat it."
> —George Santayana

> "History is written by the winners."
> —Alex Haley

> "History will be kind to me for I intend to write it."
> —Winston Churchill

> "It is sometimes very hard to tell the difference between history and the smell of skunk."
> —Rebecca West

3. **Writing** *Opinion Piece* "The Liberation of Rome" sketches what can happen when one culture dominates another. What are some of the outcomes of cultural domination suggested in the story? In a one-page opinion piece, state whether you feel yourself to be a member of a dominant or subordinate culture. Try to support your opinion with facts. What is your personal view about this situation?

# Test

## By Theodore Thomas

*"His mother's scream rang steadily in his ears. As he strained at the wheel, he wondered how a scream could go on so long."*

Robert Proctor was a good driver for so young a person. The turnpike curved gently ahead of him. Travel was light on this cool morning in May. He felt rested, but alert. He had been driving for two hours.

The sun was bright but not glaring. The air smelled fresh and clean. He breathed in deeply. It was a good day for driving.

He looked at the gray-haired woman sitting in the front seat with him. Her mouth was curved in a quiet smile. As she watched the trees and fields slip by on her side of the turnpike Robert Proctor looked back at the road. "Enjoying it, Mom?" he asked.

"Yes, Robert." Her voice was as cool as the morning.

He listened to the smooth purr of the engine. Up ahead he saw a big truck. It was spouting smoke as it sped along the turnpike. Behind it was a blue convertible, content to stay in line.

Robert Proctor noted this and put it in the back of his mind. He was slowly overtaking the car and the truck. He would reach them in another minute or two.

It was a good morning for driving. He pulled up and began to pass the blue convertible. Though his speed was a few miles an hour above the turnpike limit, his car was under perfect control.

The blue convertible suddenly swung out from behind the truck without warning. It struck his car near the right front fender. His car was knocked to the shoulder next to the turnpike median strip.

Robert Proctor was too wise to slam on the brakes. He fought the steering wheel to hold the car on a straight path. The left wheels sank into the soft left shoulder. The car seemed to pull toward the left. If it kept going that way, it might cross the island and enter the lane carrying cars coming from the other direction.

Robert held on to the steering wheel. Then the left front wheel struck a rock, and the tire blew out. The car turned sideways. It was then that his mother began to scream.

As the car turned, it skidded part way out into the oncoming lanes. Robert Proctor fought the steering wheel to right the car. But the drag of the blown tire was too much. His mother's scream rang steadily in his ears. As he strained at the wheel, he wondered how a scream could go on so long.

An oncoming car struck his car from the side, and spun him farther into the left-hand lanes.

He was thrown into his mother's lap. She was thrown against the right door. It was locked and it held. With his left hand he grabbed the steering wheel. He pulled himself up. He turned the wheel to try to stop the spin so he could get his car out of traffic. His mother could not right herself. She lay against the door, her cry rising and falling with the spin of the car.

The car began to slow down. In one of the spins, he twisted the wheel straight and headed down the left-hand lane. Before he could turn off the pike to safety, a car loomed ahead of him.

The man at the wheel of that other car seemed unable to move. His eyes were wide and filled with fear. Beside him sat a girl with her head against the back of the seat. Soft curls framed her lovely face. She was asleep.

It was not the fear in the man's face that reached Robert Proctor. It was the trust in the face of the sleeping girl. In a flash the two cars sped closer to each other. Robert Proctor had no time to change the direction of his car.

The driver of the other car remained frozen at the wheel. Robert Proctor stared into the face of the sleeping girl. His mother's cry still sounded in his ears.

He heard no crash when the two cars met head on at high speed. He only felt something push into his stomach. Then the world went gray. Just before darkness came, he heard the scream stop. He knew then that he had been hearing one single scream. It had only seemed to drag on and on.

Robert Proctor seemed to be at the bottom of a deep black well. There was a spot of faint light in the far distance. He could hear the rumble of a voice. He tried to pull himself toward the light and the sound. But the effort was too great. He lay still and gathered his strength to try again. The light grew brighter and the voice louder. When he tried again, he seemed to draw closer to the light and sound. He opened his eyes and looked at the man sitting in front of him.

"You all right, son?" asked the man. He wore a blue uniform. His round face was familiar.

Robert Proctor moved his head slowly. He discovered that he was lying back in a chair. He could move his arms and legs. He looked around the room. Then he remembered.

The man in the uniform saw the look in Robert's eyes. He said, "No harm done, son. You just took the last part of your driver's test."

Robert Proctor looked at the man. Though he saw the man clearly, he seemed to see the faint face of the sleeping girl in front of him.

The uniformed man went on talking. "We hypnotized you to make you think you were in an accident. We do it to everybody these days before they get their driver's license. Makes better drivers of them. Makes drivers more careful for the rest of their lives. Remember it now? Coming in here and all?"

Robert Proctor nodded, thinking of the sleeping girl. She never would have awakened. She would have gone from her light sleep to the dark sleep of death. Worst of all would have been his mother's death.

The uniformed man was still speaking. "So you think you're all set now. If you still want a driver's license, sign this application and we'll see."

Robert Proctor looked at the license application and signed it.

He looked up to find two men in long white coats. They were standing one on each side of him. Somehow the sight of them made him angry.

He started to speak but the uniformed man spoke first. "Sorry, son. You failed your license test. You're sick and need treatment."

The two men lifted Robert Proctor to his feet. He said, "Take your hands off me. What is this?"

The uniformed man said, "Nobody should want to drive a car after going through what you just went through. It should take months before you can even think of driving again. But you're ready to drive right now. Killing people doesn't seem to bother you. We can't let your kind run around loose any more. But don't you worry, son. They'll take good care of you. They'll fix you up." He nodded to the two men. They began to march Robert Proctor out.

At the door he spoke. His voice was so full of pleading the two men paused. "You can't really mean this," he said. "I must still be dreaming. This is all part of the test, isn't it?"

The uniformed man said, "No, son, but you can try again later." They dragged Robert out the door, knees stiff, feet dragging. As they pulled, his rubber heels slid along the two grooves worn in the floor.

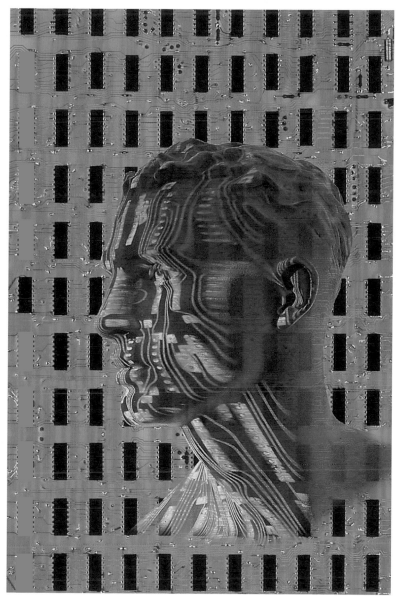

*Wired Head,* Chris Alan Wilton.

Examine this visual and describe its emotional effect. Show how that effect is created both by the subject matter and through artistic technique.

**Theodore Thomas**, American novelist, essayist, and short story writer, was born in 1920. He is best known for his science fiction writing, which has appeared in various magazines and anthologies.

**1. *Response***

**a.** "Test" is carefully constructed to offer readers a series of unexpected twists and surprises. Identify these twists and explain how the author intentionally misleads the audience in each case. As a reader, do you often know what the surprise will be before you reach it? Explain what you like better: to be surprised, or to make a guess that turns out to be right.

**b.** Is the test fair? Do you agree with the uniformed man's diagnosis of Robert at the end of the test? Give reasons for your point of view.

**c.** Explain the significance of the "two grooves" that are described at the end of the story. What inference can you draw from this detail?

**2. *Literature Studies*** *Science Fiction* Much of what we call *science fiction* depends on extrapolation. The author chooses some aspect of the present as a starting point, then exaggerates it and projects it into the future. The results often serve as a warning about where current trends might take us. In "Test," what aspects of the present does Thomas extrapolate upon? What warnings are implied by the ending of the story?

**3. *Language Conventions*** *Sentence Length* Skim the story, noting the frequency with which the author employs short, simple sentences. Choose a three-paragraph passage in which short sentences predominate and rewrite it, combining sentences to create longer and more complex structures. Read the original passage aloud and then your rewrite. Do you prefer one version over the other? Explain. What have you learned about how sentence length can affect a reader?

# Soul-Catcher

By Louis Owens

In the Mississippi swamps of the Yazoo River, a teenager learns about his Choctaw heritage—and the legend of *nalusachito* (the soul-catcher).

The old man held the rifle in one hand and walked bent over under the weight of the gunnysack on his back, as if studying the tangle of roots that was the trail. Behind him three lanky brown-and-black-and-white hounds crowded close to his thin legs and threw nervous glances at the wet forest all around. The only sound was that of the old man's boots and the occasional whine of one of the dogs. The sliver of moon had set, and the trail was very dark. The light from the carbide lamp on his hat cast a phosphorescent glow around the group, so that the old man, with his long silver hair, might have been one of the Choctaw shadows on the bright path home.

Out of the dark to the old man's right came a scream that cut through the swamp like jagged tin and sent the hounds trembling against his legs.

"Hah! Get back you!" he scolded, turning to shake his head at the cringing dogs. "That cat ain't going to eat you, not yet."

The dogs whined and pushed closer so that the old man stumbled and caught himself and the light from the headlamp splashed upon the trail. He shook his head again and chuckled, making shadows dance around them. He knew what it was that stalked him. The black *koi*[1] hadn't been seen in the swamps during the old man's lifetime, but as a child he'd heard the stories so often that he knew at once what the *koi* meant. It was an old and familiar story.

---

[1] *koi:* "panther" in Choctaw

He'd felt the black one out there in the swamps for a long time. The bird, *falachito*,[2] had called from the trees to warn him, and he had listened and gone on because what else was there to do? All of his life he had been prepared to recognize the soul-catcher when it should come.

The old man also knew that the screamer was probably the panther that the fool white man, Reeves, had wounded near Satartia a couple of weeks before. He could feel the animal's anger there in the darkness, feel the hatred like grit between his teeth. And he felt great pity for the injured cat.

The boar coon in the sack was heavy, and the old man thought that he should have brought the boy along to help, but then the forest opened and he was at the edge of his cabin clearing, seeing the thread of his garden trail between the stubble of the past year's corn and the dried husks of melon and squash vines. Behind him, this time to his left, the panther screamed again. The cat had been circling like that for the past hour, never getting any closer or any farther away.

He paused at the edge of the clearing and spoke a few words in a low voice, trying to communicate his understanding and sympathy to the wounded animal and his knowledge of what was there to the soul-catcher. For a moment he leaned the rifle against his leg and reached up to touch a small pouch that hung inside his shirt. All of his life the old man had balanced two realities, two worlds, a feat that had never struck him as particularly noteworthy or difficult. But as the cat called out once more, he felt a shadow fall over him. The animal's cry rose from the dark waters of the swamp to the stars and then fell away like one of the deep, bottomless places in the river.

When the old man pulled the leather thong to open the door, the hounds shot past and went to cower beneath the plank beds. He lowered the bag to the puncheon floor and pushed the door closed. After a moment's thought he dropped the bolt into place before reaching with one hand to hang the twenty-two on nails beneath a much larger rifle. Finally, he looked at the teenage boy sitting on the edge of one of the beds with a book in his lap. The lantern beside the boy left half of his upturned face in shadow, as if two faces met in one, but the old man could see one green eye and the fair skin, and he wondered once more how much Choctaw there was in the boy.

The boy looked up fully and stared at the old uncle. The distinct epicanthic fold of each eye giving the boy's face an oddly Oriental quality.

---

[2] *falachito:* big crow

"*Koi*," the old man said. "A painter.[3] He followed me home."

After a moment's silence, the boy said, "You going to keep him?"

The old man grinned. The boy was getting better.

"Not this one," he replied. "He's no good. A fool shot him, and now he's mad." He studied the air to one side of the boy and seemed to make a decision. "Besides, this black one may be *nalusachito*,[4] the soul-catcher. He's best left alone, I think."

The boy's grin died quickly, and the old man saw fear and curiosity mingle in the pale eyes.

"Why do you think it's *nalusachito?*" The word was awkward on the boy's tongue.

"Sometimes you just know these things. He's been out there a while. The bird warned me, and now that fool white man has hurt him."

"*Nalusachito* is just a myth," the boy said.

The old man looked at the book in the boy's lap. "You reading that book again?"

The boy nodded.

"A teacher give that book to your dad one time, so's he could learn all about his people, the teacher said. He used to read that book, too, and tell me about us Choctaws." The old man grinned once more. "After he left, I read some of that book."

The old man reached a hand toward the boy. "Here, let me read you the part I like best about us people." He lifted a pair of wire-rimmed glasses from a shelf above the rifles and slipped them on.

The boy held the book out and the old man took it. Bending so that the lantern-light fell across the pages, he thumbed expertly through the volume.

"This is a good book, all right. Tells us all about ourselves. This writer was a smart man. Listen to this." He began to read, pronouncing each word with care, as though it were a foreign language.

> *The Choctaw warrior, as I knew him in his native Mississippi forest, was as fine a specimen of manly perfection as I have ever beheld.*

He looked up with a wink.

---

[3]**painter:** in the old man's dialect, he pronounces "panther" as "painter."
[4]**nalusachito:** literally, "the big black thing" (na=thing, lusa=black, chito=big)

*He seemed to be as perfect as the human form could be. Tall,*
*beautiful in symmetry of form and face, graceful, active,*
*straight, fleet, with lofty and independent bearing, he seemed*
*worthy in saying, as he of Juan Fernández fame: "I am monarch*
*of all I survey." His black piercing eye seemed to penetrate and*
*read the very thoughts of the heart, while his firm step proclaimed*
*a feeling sense of manly independence. Nor did their women fall*
*behind in all that pertains to female beauty.*

The old man looked at the boy. "Now there's a man that hit the nail on the head." He paused for a moment. "You ever heard of this Juan Fernández? Us Choctaws didn't get along too good with Spanish people in the old days. Remind me to tell you about Tuscaloosa sometime."

The boy shook his head. "Alabama?"

The old man nodded. "I read this next part to Old Lady Blue Wood that lives 'crost the river. She says this is the smartest white man she ever heard of." He adjusted the glasses and read again.

*They were of such unnatural beauty that they literally appeared*
*to light up everything around them. Their shoulders were broad*
*and their carriage true to Nature, which has never been excelled*
*by the hand of art, their long, black tresses hung in flowing waves,*
*extending nearly to the ground; but the beauty of the countenances*
*of many of those Choctaw and Chickasaw girls was so extraordinary*
*that if such faces were seen today in one of the parlors of the*
*fashionable world, they would be considered as a type of beauty*
*hitherto unknown.*

He handed the book back to the boy and removed the glasses, grinning all the while. "Now parts of that do sound like Old Lady Blue Wood. That unnatural part, and that part about broad shoulders. But she ain't never had a carriage that I know of, and she's more likely to light into anybody that's close than to light 'em up."

The boy looked down at the moldy book and then grinned weakly back at the old uncle. Beneath the floppy hat, surrounded by the acrid smell of the carbide headlamp, the old man seemed like one of the swamp shadows come into the cabin. The boy thought about his father, the old man's nephew, who had been only half Choctaw but looked nearly as dark and indestructible as the uncle. Then he looked down at his own hand in the light from the kerosene lantern. The pale skin embarrassed him, gave him away. The old man, his great-uncle, was Indian, and his father had been Indian, but he wasn't.

There was a thud on the wood shingles of the cabin's roof. Dust fell from each of the four corners of the cabin and onto the pages of the damp book.

"*Nalusachito* done climbed up on the roof," the old man said, gazing at the ceiling with amusement. "He moves pretty good for a cat that's hurt, don't he?"

The boy knew the uncle was watching for his reaction. He steeled himself, and then the panther screamed and he flinched.

The old man nodded. "Only a fool or a crazy man ain't scared when soul-catcher's walking around on his house," he said.

"You're not afraid," the boy replied, watching as the old man set the headlamp on a shelf and hung the wide hat on a nail beside the rifles.

The old man pulled a piece of canvas from beneath the table and spread it on the floor. As he dumped the coon out onto the canvas, he looked up with a chuckle. "That book says Choctaw boys always respected their elders. I'm scared alright, but I know about that cat, you see, and that's the difference. That cat ain't got no surprises for me because I'm old, and I done heard all the stories."

The boy glanced at the book.

"It don't work that way," the old man said. "You can't read them. A white man comes and he pokes around and pays somebody, or maybe somebody feels sorry for him and tells him stuff and he writes it down. But he don't understand, so he can't put it down right, you see."

How do you understand? the boy wanted to ask as he watched the uncle pull a knife from its sheath on his hip and begin to skin the coon, making cuts down each leg and up the belly so delicately that the boy could see no blood at all. The panther shrieked overhead, and the old man seemed not to notice.

"Why don't you shoot it?" the boy asked, looking at the big deer rifle on the wall, the thirty-forty Krag from the Spanish-American War.

The old man looked up in surprise.

"You could sell the skin to Mr. Wheeler for a lot of money, couldn't you?" Mr. Wheeler was the black man who came from across the river to buy the coonskins.

The old man squinted and studied the boy's face. "You can't hunt that cat," he said patiently. "*Nalusachito's* something you got to accept, something that's just there."

"You see," he continued, "what folks like that fool Reeves don't understand is that this painter has always been out there. We just ain't noticed him for a long time. He's always there, and that's what people forget. You can't kill him." He tapped his chest with the handle of the knife. "*Nalusachito* comes from in here."

The boy watched the old man in silence. He knew about the soul-catcher from the book in his lap. It was an old superstition, and the book didn't say anything about *nalusachito* being a panther. That was something the old man invented. This panther was very real and dangerous. He looked skeptically at the old man and then up at the rifle.

"No," the old man said. "We'll just let this painter be."

He pulled the skin off over the head of the raccoon like a sweater, leaving the naked body shining like a baby in the yellow light. Under the beds the dogs sniffed and whined, and overhead the whispers moved across the roof.

The old man held the skin up and admired it, then laid it fur-side down on the bench beside him. "I sure ain't going outside to nail this up right now," he said, the corners of his mouth suggesting a grin. He lifted the bolt and pushed the door open and swung the body of the coon out into the dark. When he closed the door there was a snarl and an impact on the ground. The dogs began to growl and whimper, and the old man said, "You, Yvonne! Hoyo!" and the dogs shivered in silence.

The boy watched the old man wash his hands in the bucket and sit on the edge of the other bed to pull off his boots. Each night and morning since he'd come it had been the same. The old uncle would go out at night and come back before daylight with something in the bag. Usually the boy would waken to find the old man in the other plank bed, sleeping like a small child, so lightly that the boy could not see or hear him breathe. But this night the boy had awakened in the very early morning, torn from sleep by a sound he wasn't conscious of hearing, and he had sat up with the lantern and book to await the old man's return. He read the book because there was nothing else to read. The myths reminded him of fairy tales he'd read as a child, and he tried to imagine his father reading them.

The old man was a real Choctaw—*Chahta okla*—a full-blood. Was the ability to believe the myths diluted with the blood, the boy wondered, so that his father could, when he had been alive, believe only half as strongly as the old man and he, his father's son, half as much yet? He thought of the soul-catcher, and he shivered, but he knew that he was just scaring himself the way kids always did. His mother had told him how they said that when his father was born the uncle had shown up at the sharecropper's cabin and announced that the boy would be his responsibility. That was the Choctaw way, he said, the right way. A man must accept responsibility for and teach his sister's children. Nobody had thought of that custom for a long time, and nobody had seen the uncle for years, and nobody knew how he'd even learned of the boy's birth, but there he was come out of the swamps across the river with his straight black hair hanging to his shoulders under the floppy hat and his face dark as night so that the mother, his sister, screamed when she saw him. And from that day onward the uncle had come often from the swamps to take the boy's father with him, to teach him.

The old man rolled into the bed, pulled the wool blanket to his chin, turned to the wall, and was asleep. The boy watched him and then turned down the lamp until only a dim glow outlined the objects in the room. He thought of Los Angeles, the bone-dry hills and yellow air, the home where he'd lived with his parents before the accident that killed both. It was difficult to be Choctaw, to be Indian there, and he'd seen his father working hard at it, growing his black hair long, going to urban powwows where the fancy dancers spun like beautiful birds. His father had taught him to hunt in the desert hills and to say a few phrases, like *Chahta isht ia*[5] and *Chahta yakni*,[6] in the old language. The words had remained only sounds, the powwow dancers only another Southern California spectacle for a green-eyed, fair-skinned boy. But the hunting had been real, a testing of desire and reflex he had felt all the way through.

Indians were hunters. Indians lived close to the land. His father had said those things often. He thought about the panther. The old man would not hunt the black cat, and had probably made up the story about *nalusachito* as an excuse. The panther was dangerous. For a month the boy had been at the cabin and had not ventured beyond the edges of the garden except to go out in the small rowboat onto the muddy Yazoo River that flanked one side of the clearing. The swampy forest around the cabin was like the river, a place in which nothing was ever clear: shadows, swirls, dark forms rising and disappearing again, nothing ever clearly seen. And each night he'd lain in the bed and listened to the booming and cracking of the swamp like something monstrously evil and thought of the old man killing things in the dark, picturing the old man as a solitary light cutting the darkness.

The panther might remain, its soft feet whispering maddeningly on the cabin roof each night while the old man hunted in the swamp. Or it might attack the old man who would not shoot it. For the first time the boy realized the advantage in not being really Choctaw. The old uncle could not hunt the panther, but he could, because he knew the cat for what it really was. It would not be any more difficult to kill than

---

[5]*Chahta isht ia:* I am Choctaw
[6]*Chahta yakni:* Choctaw land

the wild pigs he'd hunted with his father in the coastal range of California, and it was no different than the cougars that haunted those same mountains. The black one was only a freak of nature.

Moving softly, he lifted the heavy rifle from its nails. In a crate on the floor he found the cartridges and, slipping on his red-plaid mackinaw, he dropped the bullets into his pocket. Then he walked carefully to the door, lifted the bolt, stepped through, and silently pulled the door closed. Outside, it was getting close to dawn and the air had the clean, raw smell of that hour, tainted by the sharp odor of the river and swamp. The trees were unsure outlines protruding from the wall of black that surrounded the cabin on three sides. Over the river the fog hovered in a gray somewhat lighter than the air, and a kingfisher called in a shrill *kree* out across the water.

He pushed shells into the rifle's magazine and then stepped along the garden trail toward the trees, listening carefully for the sounds of the woods. Where even he knew there should have been the shouting of crickets, frogs, and a hundred other night creatures, there was only silence beating like the heartbeat drum at one of the powwows. At the edge of the clearing he paused.

In the cabin the old man sat up and looked toward the door. The boy had an hour before full daylight, and he would meet *nalusachito* in that transitional time. The old man fingered the medicine pouch on the cord around his neck and wondered about such a convergence. There was a meaning beyond his understanding, something that could not be avoided.

The boy brushed aside a muskedine vine and stepped into the woods, feeling his boots sink into the wet floor. It had all been a singular journey toward this, out of the light of California, across the burning earth of the Southwest, and into the darkness of this place. Beyond the garden, in the uncertain light, the trunks of trees, the brush and vines were like a curtain closing behind him. Then the panther cried in the damp woods somewhere in front of him, the sound insinuating itself into the night like one of the tendrils of fog that clung to the ground. The boy began to walk on the faint trail toward the sound, the air so thick he felt as though he were suspended in fluid, his movements like those of a man walking on the floor of the sea. His breathing became torturous and liquid, and his eyes adjusted to the darkness and strained to isolate the watery forms surrounding him.

When he had gone a hundred yards the panther called again, a strange, dreamlike, muted cry different from the earlier screams, and he hesitated a moment and then left the trail to follow the cry. A form slid from the trail beside his boot, and he moved carefully away, deeper into the woods beyond the trail. Now the light was graying, and the leaves and bark of the trees became delicately etched as the day broke.

The close scream of the panther jerked him into full consciousness, and he saw the cat. Twenty feet away, it crouched in a clutter of vines and brush, its yellow eyes burning at him. In front of the panther was the half-eaten carcass of the coon.

He raised the rifle slowly, bringing it to his shoulder and slipping the safety off in the same movement. With his action, the panther pushed itself upright until it sat on its haunches, facing him. It was then the boy saw that one of the front feet hung limp, a festering wound in the shoulder on that side. He lined the notched sight of the rifle against the cat's head, and he saw the burning go out of the eyes. The panther watched him calmly, waiting as he pulled the trigger. The animal toppled backward, kicked for an instant and was still.

He walked to the cat and nudged it with a boot. *Nalusachito* was dead. He leaned the rifle against a tree and lifted the cat by its four feet and swung it onto his back, surprised at how light it was and feeling the sharp edges of the ribs through the fur. He felt sorrow and pity for the hurt animal he could imagine hunting awkwardly in the swamps, and he knew that what he had done was right. He picked up the rifle and turned back toward the cabin.

When he opened the cabin door, with the cat on his shoulder, the old man was sitting in the chair facing him. The boy leaned the rifle against the bench and swung the panther carefully to the floor and looked up at the old man, but the old man's eyes were fixed on the open doorway. Beyond the doorway *nalusachito* crouched, ready to spring.

**Louis Owens** was born in Lompoc, California, of Choctaw, Cherokee, and Irish American heritage. He worked as a forest ranger and firefighter for the Forest Service, before obtaining his Ph.D. from the University of California. He has lectured in Italy, was Professor of Literature at the University of California, Santa Cruz, and Professor of English at the University of New Mexico, Albuquerque. His works include the novels *The Sharpest Sight* and *Wolfsong*, as well as several critical studies.

**1. *Response***

**a.** What atmosphere is created by the descriptive details in the opening four paragraphs? What specific details serve to create suspense?

**b.** Who do you think is the protagonist of the story—the old man or the boy? Explain.

**c.** In your view, why has the author refrained from naming the characters?

**d.** The conclusion of "Soul-Catcher" is *open-ended,* open to interpretation. What is your own interpretation of what happens? Do you enjoy stories that are open-ended, or do you prefer stories in which the message is clear and all the loose ends are tied up? Why?

**2. *Literature Studies*** *Conflict*  In a small group, list the different kinds of conflict that occur in the story, both external and internal. For each one, discuss whether it was resolved, and if so, how. Try to reach a consensus about what is the most important or interesting conflict.

**3. *Language Conventions*** *Quotations*  Examine the three quotations on pages 137 and 138 of the story, and identify how they have been specially treated to make them stand out from the rest of the story. Use a style guide or other reference work to find out the usual rules for presenting quotations. Following these rules, show an alternative way of presenting the first quotation. Find a piece of your own writing that includes quotations. Does your presentation of quotations fit the rules?

**4. *Making Connections*** In what ways is the boy similar to the narrator in "A Secret Lost in the Water"? What other similarities are there between the two stories?

# Wilhelm

By Gabrielle Roy

*"My mother at once forbade me to return to the O'Neills, so long, said she, as I had not got over the idea of Wilhelm."*

**M**y first suitor came from Holland. He was called Wilhelm and his teeth were too regular; he was much older than I; he had a long, sad face...at least thus it was that others made me see him when they had taught me to consider his defects. As for me, at first I found his face thoughtful rather than long and peaked. I did not yet know that his teeth—so straight and even—were false. I thought I loved Wilhelm. Here was the first man who, through me, could be made happy or unhappy; here was a very serious matter.

I had met him at our friends' the O'Neills', who still lived not far from us in their large gabled house on Rue Desmeurons. Wilhelm was their boarder; for life is full of strange things: thus this big, sad man was a chemist in the employ of a small paint factory then operating in our city, and—as I have said—lodged with equally uprooted people, the O'Neills, formerly of County Cork in Ireland. A far journey to have come merely to behave, in the end, like everyone else—earn your living, try to make friends, learn our language, and then, in Wilhelm's case, love someone who was not for him. Do adventures often turn out so tritely? Obviously enough, though, in those days I did not think so.

Evenings at the O'Neills' were musical. Kathleen played "Mother Machree," while her mother, seated on a sofa, wiped her eyes, trying the while to avert our attention, to direct it away from herself, for she did not like people to believe her so deeply stirred by Irish songs. Despite the music, Elizabeth kept right on digging away at her arithmetic; she still was utterly indifferent to men. But Kathleen and I cared a great deal. We feared dreadfully to be left on the shelf; we feared we should fail to be loved and to love with a great and absolutely unique passion.

When Mrs. O'Neill requested it of me—"to relieve the atmosphere," as she put it—I played Paderewski's "Minuet"; then Wilhelm would have us listen to Massenet on a violin of choice quality. Afterward he would show me in an album scenes of his country, as well as his father's house and the home of his uncle, his father's partner. I think he was anxious to convey to me that his family was better off than you might think if you judged by him—I mean by his having had to quit his native land and come live in our small city. Yet he need have had no fear that I should form an opinion on the basis of silly social appearances; I wanted to judge people in strict accordance with their noble personal qualities. Wilhelm would explain to me how Ruisdael had really most faithfully rendered the full, sad sky of the Low Countries; and he asked me whether I thought I should like Holland enough one day to visit it. Yes, I replied; I should much like to see the canals and the tulip fields.

Then he had had sent to me from Holland a box of chocolates, each one of which was a small vial containing a liqueur.

But one evening he had the ill-starred notion of accompanying me back home, as far as our front door, though it was only two steps away and darkness had not wholly fallen. He was chivalrous: he insisted that a man should not let a woman go home all alone, even if that woman only yesterday had still been playing with hoops or walking on stilts.

Alas! The moment his back was turned, Maman asked me about my young man. "Who is that great beanstalk?"

I told her it was Wilhelm of Holland, and all the rest of it: the box of chocolates, the tulip fields, the stirring sky of Wilhelm's country, the windmills…. Now all that was fine and honorable! But why, despite what I thought of appearances, did I believe myself obliged also to speak of the uncle and the father, partners in a small business which … which … made a lot of money?

My mother at once forbade me to return to the O'Neills, so long, said she, as I had not got over the idea of Wilhelm.

But Wilhelm was clever. One or two days each week he finished work early; on those days he waited for me at the convent door. He took over my great bundle of books—Lord, what homework the Sisters piled on us in those days!—my music sheets, my metronome, and he carried all these burdens to the corner of our street. There he would lower upon me his large and sad blue eyes and say to me, "When you are bigger, I'll take you to the opera, to the theater…."

I still had two years of the convent ahead of me; the opera, the theater seemed desperately far away. Wilhelm would tell me that he longed to see me in an evening gown; that then he would at last remove from its moth-proof bag his dress clothes and that we should go in style to hear symphonic music.

My mother ultimately learned that Wilhelm had the effrontery to carry my books, and it annoyed her very much. She forbade me to see him.

"Still," said I to Maman, "I can hardly prevent his walking next to me along the pavement."

My mother cut through that problem. "If he takes the same sidewalk as you, mind you cross right over to the other."

Now, she must have sent a message of rebuke to Wilhelm and told him, as she had me, precisely which sidewalk he should take, for I began seeing him only on the opposite side of the street, where he would stolidly await my passage. All the while I was going by, he held his hat in his hand. The other young girls must have been horribly envious of me; they laughed at Wilhelm's baring his head while I was passing. Yet I felt death in my soul at seeing Wilhelm so alone and exposed to ridicule. He was an immigrant, and Papa had told me a hundred times that you could not have too much sympathy, too much consideration for the uprooted, who have surely suffered enough from their expatriation without our adding to it through scorn or disdain. Why then had Papa so completely changed his views, and why was he more set even than Maman against Wilhelm of Holland? True enough, no one at home, since Georgianna's marriage, looked favorably upon love. Perhaps because as a whole we had already had too much to suffer from it. But I—presumably—I had not yet suffered enough at its hands....

And then, as I have said, Wilhelm was clever. Maman had forbidden him to speak to me on the street, but she had forgotten letters. Wilhelm had made great progress in English. He sent me very beautiful epistles which began with: "My own beloved child..." or else "Sweet little maid...." Not to be outdone, I replied: "My own dearest heart ...." One day my mother found in my room a scrawl on which I had been practising my handwriting and in which I expressed to Wilhelm a passion that neither time nor cruel obstacles could bend.... Had my mother glanced into the volume of Tennyson lying open upon my table, she would have recognized the whole passage in question, but she was far too angry to listen to reason. I was enjoined from writing to Wilhelm, from reading his letters, if, by a miracle, one of them succeeded in penetrating the defenses thrown up by Maman; I was even enjoined from thinking of him. I was allowed only to pray for him, if I insisted upon it.

Until then I had thought that love should be open and clear, cherished by all and making peace between beings. Yet what was happening? Maman was turned into something like a spy, busy with poking about in my wastebasket; and I then thought that she was certainly the last person in the world to understand me! So that was what love accomplished! And where was that fine frankness between Maman and me! Does there always arise a bad period between a mother and her daughter? Is it love that brings it on?... And what, what is love? One's neighbor? Or some person rich, beguiling?

During this interval Wilhelm, unable to do anything else for me, sent me many gifts; and at the time I knew nothing of them, for the moment they arrived, Maman would return them to him: music scores, tulip bulbs from Amsterdam, a small collar of Bruges lace, more liqueur-filled chocolates.

The only means left to us by which to communicate was the telephone. Maman had not thought of that. Obviously she could not think of everything; love is so crafty! Then, too, during her loving days the telephone did not exist, and this, I imagine, was why Maman forgot to ban it for me. Wilhelm often called our number. If it was not I who answered, he hung up gently. And many a time did Maman then protest, "What's going on?... I shall write the company a letter; I'm constantly being bothered for nothing. At the other end I can barely hear a sort of sighing sound." Naturally she could not foresee how far the tenacity of a Wilhelm would extend.

But when it was I who answered, Wilhelm was scarcely better off. There could be between us no real conversation without its exposing us to the discovery of our secret and consequent prohibition of the telephone. Moreover, we neither of us had any taste for ruses; Gervais employed them when he had on the wire the darling of his heart, to whom he spoke as though she were another schoolboy. But Wilhelm and I—without blaming Gervais, for love is love, and when it encounters obstacles, is even more worthy!—we strove to be noble in all things. Thus Wilhelm merely murmured to me, from afar, "Dear heart ..." after which he remained silent. And I listened to his silence for a minute or two, blushing to the roots of my hair.

One day, though, he discovered an admirable way to make me understand his heart. As I was saying "Allo!" his voice begged me to hold the wire; then I made out something like the sound of a violin being tuned, then the opening bars of "Thaïs."[1] Wilhelm played me the whole composition over the phone. Kathleen must have been accompanying him. I heard piano chords somewhere in the distance, and—I know not why—this put me out a trifle, perhaps at thinking that Kathleen was in on so lovely a secret. It was the first time, however, that Wilhelm put me out at all.

---

[1] **"Thaïs":** A mournful composition for violin and piano, from the opera *Thaïs*, by the French composer Jules Massenet (1842–1912). It is just under five minutes long.

Our phone was attached to the wall at the end of a dark little hall-way. At first no one was surprised at seeing me spend hours there, motionless and in the most complete silence. Only little by little did the people at home begin to notice that at the telephone I uttered no word. And from then on, when I went to listen to "Thaïs" the hall door would open slightly; someone hid there to spy on me, motioning the others to advance one by one and watch me. Gervais was the worst, and it was very mean on his part, for I had respected his secret. He manu-factured reasons for making use of the hall; as he went by he tried to hear what I could be listening to. At first, however, I held the receiver firmly glued to my ear. Then I must already have begun to find "Thaïs" very long to hear through. One evening I allowed Gervais to listen for a moment to Wilhelm's music; perhaps I hoped that he would have enough enthusiasm to make me myself admire the composition. But Gervais choked with mirth; later on I saw him playing the fool in front of the others, at the far end of the living room, bowing an imagi-nary violin. Even Maman laughed a little, although she tried to remain angry. With a long, sad countenance which—I knew not how—he superimposed upon his own features, Gervais was giving a fairly good imitation of Wilhelm in caricature. I was a little tempted to laugh. For it is a fact that there is something quite comic in seeing a sad person play the violin.

When you consider it, it is astonishing that all of them together should not have thought much sooner of parting me from Wilhelm by the means they so successfully employed from that night forward.

All day long, when I went by, someone was whistling the melody of "Thaïs."

My brother grossly exaggerated the Dutchman's slightly solemn gait, his habit of keeping his eyes lifted aloft. They discovered in him the mien of a Protestant minister, dry—said they—and in the process of preparing a sermon. Maman added that the "Netherlander" had a face as thin as a knife blade. This was the way they now referred to him: the "Netherlander" or the "Hollander." My sister Odette—I should say Sister Edouard—who had been informed and was taking a hand in the matter, even though she had renounced the world, my pious Odette herself told me to forget the "foreigner"... that a foreigner is a foreigner....

One evening as I listened to "Thaïs," I thought I must look silly, standing thus stock still, the receiver in my hand. I hung up before the end of the performance.

Thereafter, Wilhelm scarcely crossed my path again.

A year later, perhaps, we learned that he was returning to Holland.

My mother once more became the just and charitable pre-Wilhelm person I had loved so dearly. My father no longer harbored anything against Holland. Maman admitted that Mrs. O'Neill had told her concerning Wilhelm that he was the best man in the world, reliable, a worker, very gentle…. And Maman hoped that Wilhelm, in his own country, among his own people, would be loved… as, she said, he deserved to be.

**Gabrielle Roy** was born in Saint-Boniface, Manitoba in 1909. She held various teaching posts in Canada, then studied drama in Europe. On her return to Canada, she settled in Montréal, where she worked as a freelance reporter. She won three Governor General's Awards for her writing. All of her works were first written in French, then translated into English.

**1. *Response***

    **a.** Reread the opening two paragraphs and find details that foreshadow the doomed nature of the relationship between Wilhelm and the narrator. Why do you think the author included these hints about the ending?

    **b.** Why does the narrator's family disapprove of Wilhelm?

    **c.** What tactic ultimately succeeds in parting the narrator from Wilhelm? What advice might have helped the narrator resist this tactic?

    **d.** Identify specific attitudes and ideas expressed by the characters in "Wilhelm" that might be regarded as unacceptable in today's society. Which attitudes and ideas does the narrator reject, and which does she accept?

**2. *Oral Language*** Prepare a two-minute oral presentation in which you argue for or against the following statement:

    It was the mother's responsibility to intervene in her daughter's life as she did.

In your presentation, you should express your personal point of view and provide strong arguments to support it. Include specific references from the story.

3. **Literature Studies** *Theme*  The main purpose of some literature is to present an important **theme** for the reader to ponder. In your own words, sum up the theme of this story in a single sentence. Reread the story to locate the three sentences or passages that, in your view, are most important in expressing the theme. Explain your choices. Conclude by telling whether the theme is important to you personally.

---

A **theme** is a central thesis or idea that is expressed directly or indirectly in a literary work.

4. **Language Conventions** *Ellipses*  Using quotations from the story, show two different functions ellipses can serve. As well, explain how the author has used ellipses to reveal something important about the narrator's character.

# He-y, Come on Ou-t!

## By Shinichi Hoshi

*Translated from the Japanese by Stanleigh Jones*

*Who would have thought that something as simple as a hole in the ground could prove to be so useful?*

The typhoon had passed and the sky was a gorgeous blue. Even a certain village not far from the city had suffered damage. A little distance from the village and near the mountains, a small shrine had been swept away by a landslide.

"I wonder how long that shrine's been here."

"Well, in any case, it must have been here since an awfully long time ago."

"We've got to rebuild it right away."

While the villagers exchanged views, several more of their number came over.

"It sure was wrecked."

"I think it used to be right here."

"No, looks like it was a little more over there."

Just then one of them raised his voice. "Hey what in the world is this hole?"

Where they had all gathered there was a hole about a meter in diameter. They peered in, but it was so dark nothing could be seen. However, it gave one the feeling that it was so deep it went clear through to the center of the earth.

There was even one person who said, "I wonder if it's a fox's hole."

"Hey-y, come on ou-t!" shouted a young man into the hole. There was no echo from the bottom. Next he picked up a pebble and was about to throw it in.

"You might bring down a curse on us. Lay off," warned an old man, but the younger one energetically threw the pebble in. As before, however, there was no answering response from the bottom. The villagers cut down some trees, tied them with rope and made a fence which they put around the hole. Then they repaired to the village.

"What do you suppose we ought to do?"

"Shouldn't we build the shrine up just as it was, over the hole?"

A day passed with no agreement. The news traveled fast, and a car from the newspaper company rushed over. In no time a scientist came out, and with an all-knowing expression on his face he went over to the hole. Next, a bunch of gawking curiosity seekers showed up; one could also pick out here and there men of shifty glances who appeared to be concessionaires. Concerned that someone might fall into the hole, a policeman from the local sub-station kept a careful watch.

One newspaper reporter tied a weight to the end of a long cord and lowered it into the hole. A long way down it went. The cord ran out, however, and he tried to pull it out, but it would not come back up. Two or three people helped out, but when they all pulled too hard, the cord parted at the edge of the hole. Another reporter, a camera in hand, who had been watching all of this, quietly untied a stout rope that had been wound around his waist.

The scientist contacted people at his laboratory and had them bring out a high-powered bull horn, with which he was going to check out the echo from the hole's bottom. He tried switching through various sounds, but there was no echo. The scientist was puzzled, but he could not very well give up with everyone watching him so intently. He put the bull horn right up to the hole, turned it to its highest volume, and let it sound continuously for a long time. It was a noise that would have carried several dozen kilometers above ground. But the hole just calmly swallowed up the sound.

In his own mind the scientist was at a loss, but with a look of apparent composure he cut off the sound and, in a manner suggesting that the whole thing had a perfectly plausible explanation, said simply, "Fill it in."

Safer to get rid of something one didn't understand.

The onlookers, disappointed that this was all that was going to happen, prepared to disperse. Just then one of the concessionaires, having broken through the throng and come forward, made a proposal.

"Let me have that hole. I'll fill it in for you."

"We'd be grateful to you for filling it in," replied the mayor of the village, "but we can't very well give you the hole. We have to build a shrine there."

"If it's a shrine you want, I'll build you a fine one later. Shall I make it with an attached meeting hall?"

Before the mayor could answer, the people of the village all shouted out.

"Really? Well, in that case, we ought to have it closer to the village."

"It's just an old hole. We'll give it to you!"

So it was settled. And the mayor, of course, had no objection.

The concessionaire was true to his promise. It was small, but closer to the village he did build for them a shrine with an attached meeting hall.

About the time the autumn festival was held at the new shrine, the hole-filling company established by the concessionaire hung out its small shingle at a shack near the hole.

The concessionaire had his cohorts mount a loud campaign in the city. "We've got a fabulously deep hole! Scientists say it's at least five thousand meters deep! Perfect for the disposal of such things as waste from nuclear reactors."

Government authorities granted permission. Nuclear power plants fought for contracts. The people of the village were a bit worried about this, but they consented when it was explained that there would be absolutely no above-ground contamination for several thousand years and that they would share in the profits. Into the bargain, very shortly a magnificent road was built from the city to the village.

Trucks rolled in over the road, transporting lead boxes. Above the hole the lids were opened, and the wastes from nuclear reactors tumbled away into the hole.

From the Foreign Ministry and the Defense Agency boxes of unnecessary classified documents were brought for disposal. Officials who came to supervise the disposal held discussions on golf. The lesser functionaries, as they threw in the papers, chatted about pinball.

The hole showed no signs of filling up. It was awfully deep, thought some; or else it might be very spacious at the bottom. Little by little the hole-filling company expanded its business.

Reading makes immigrants of us all. It takes us away from home, but more important, it finds homes for us everywhere.

Hazel Rochman

Bodies of animals used in contagious disease experiments at the universities were brought out, and to these were added the unclaimed corpses of vagrants. Better than dumping all of its garbage in the ocean, went the thinking in the city, and plans were made for a long pipe to carry it to the hole.

The hole gave peace of mind to the dwellers of the city. They concentrated solely on producing one thing after another. Everyone disliked thinking about the eventual consequences. People wanted only to work for production companies and sales corporations; they had no interest in becoming junk dealers. But, it was thought, these problems too would gradually be resolved by the hole.

Young girls discarded old diaries in the hole. There were also those who were inaugurating new love affairs and threw into the hole old photographs of themselves taken with former sweethearts. The police felt comforted as they used the hole to get rid of accumulations of expertly done counterfeit bills. Criminals breathed easier after throwing material evidence into the hole.

Whatever one wished to discard, the hole accepted it all. The hole cleansed the city of its filth; the sea and sky seemed to have become a bit clearer than before.

Aiming at the heavens, new buildings went on being constructed one after the other.

One day, atop the high steel frame of a new building under construction, a workman was taking a break. Above his head he heard a voice shout:

"He-y, come on ou-t!"

But, in the sky to which he lifted his gaze there was nothing at all. A clear blue sky merely spread over all. He thought it must be his imagination. Then, as he resumed his former position, from the direction where the voice had come, a small pebble skimmed by him and fell on past.

The man, however, was gazing in idle reverie at the city's skyline growing ever more beautiful, and he failed to notice.

Tokyo-born **Shinichi Hoshi** (1926–1997) was one of Japan's most prolific science fiction writers. During his career, he wrote well over a thousand short stories.

## 1. *Response*

**a.** When the hole was first discovered, the villagers debated about what they should do with it. Why is it significant that their first plan involved rebuilding the shrine?

**b.** What obvious theme does this story present? What do you think the author, Shinichi Hoshi, might have been trying to achieve with this story?

**c.** Briefly describe your reaction to "He-y, Come on Ou-t!" Do you think the author would have been pleased with your reaction? Explain.

## 2. *Literature Studies* Symbolism

This story is a fantasy. It invites readers to reach beyond the literal level and explore its **symbolic meaning**. With this in mind, work in a group to make a list of the important characters, details, and events of the story. Try to reach a consensus about what each item on the list might symbolize in the real world.

The **symbolic meaning** of a work is developed through the symbols the author includes. A *symbol* is something that represents something else—for example, the lion can be a symbol of courage.

## 3. *Media* Persuasion

The media are full of persuasive messages about the environment. With a partner, collect examples of these messages. Try to take examples from different media, and/or look for different viewpoints and approaches. For each example, summarize where you found it, who generated it, what its message is, and what audience you think it is trying to influence. State which message is most persuasive and explain how you reached that conclusion.

"He is *loco,
este hombre,*
a little crazy."

# The Singing Silence

By Eva-Lis Wuorio

Old Vicente of Formentera was perhaps the happiest man I've ever known. And also, perhaps, the poorest.

He was a cadaverous, bent juniper of a man, brown and lined, and he owned not one piece of clothing that was not patched. He lived at Cala Pujol, in a lean-to made of stone and driftwood and brush, with a rusty iron brazier for his kitchen and a couple of cracked iron pots, discarded by the fishermen, from which to eat. But he owned also an excellent snorkel and a pair of rubber flippers and a diver's mask, and, as I say, I don't believe there was a happier man.

I had been coming to Formentera for several years before Vicente stood out in my eyes from the old fishermen who drew their boats up under the brush and the bamboo shelters at the end of the beach where the rocks begin. At last I realized he was not a fisherman. He had no time to fish.

I had some Ibicenco, his dialect, a language quite different from the Castilian Spanish, so I could tell, that day I first saw him, that he was asking with dignity, not pleading, for the loan of a fisherman's small boat. I could not understand, thinking him a fisherman, how he got along without a boat, but I offered to lend him the one I always rent in Formentera. I do not use it often anyhow. He thanked me, and again his dignity impressed me.

I watched him load the boat with the snorkel and the flippers and the face mask, an earthen jug of water, and a small parcel of provisions. There was no fishing gear, no underwater gun to go with his other equipment. I wondered what he intended to catch and how. I watched him row out, facing the horizon, a small man, intent.

I watched until he was but a speck on the horizon, and then I forgot about him. At Cala Pujol it is easy to forget. The turquoise waters are deep and clear to the bottom, the sand is untrodden, there is a long sweep of white-silver shore—the year I speak of, it was still that way—and the sun is a constant benediction. In peace, one forgets.

There came a day when the wind blew from Africa and the sea was sultry and the fishermen did not go out. They sat in the bamboo-roofed little bar on the beach and drank red wine and talked. "Vicente got in?"

"Not yet."

"He is *loco, este hombre*, a little crazy."

"Not at all, not so much. He has the good intention."

"You think so? You, too, are *loco*."

"Me? Not at all. I see the point. I understand very well."

"Vicente?" I asked. "He is the old man with the underwater equipment?"

"Ah," they said, "aha. Ah."

I asked for another bottle of the wine of the island, for only that is drunk there. We do not try to be smart by taking better-known wines.

And, so sitting there, with the wind from Africa blowing and stirring up the sea until it was muddy below and racing, sheep-white, above, I heard the story of Vicente.

He had been an ambitious boy 60 years ago, and he had left Formentera, the little island of the past. But 60 years ago there was not much for a Spaniard to do in his country of Spain. So Vicente went to sea in foreign ships, and after a time he came back. He walked the country, trying all sorts of jobs, but he ended where better men than he had ended, as a porter on the quays of Barcelona—a *mozo*.

He had had a dream, but dreams fail a man sometimes. So he carried the luggage of others: the rich Spaniards, the visitors, the tourists. Until ten years ago he stood there at the quay, a number on his hat, waving his hand at the passengers from the boats, pointing to himself and shouting, "Me? Me! Number Seventy-three!"

One day a rich American from a Palma boat saw his frantic wave and beckoned. Vicente got in line with the other porters and pushed his way up the gangplank to the white boat. There this rich American said to him, "Here are six suitcases, and that thing. Be careful with it; it's an antique."

Vicente recognized the earthen vessel. It was an amphora, a Phœnician one, a fine, rare specimen of the big jugs used for transporting wine or grain. In the old days fishermen sometimes caught them in their nets. They had often thrown them back into the sea, but this they did no longer, not since the *señores* from the town came to buy them for their museums.

Vicente hoisted the bags on his back, picked up the big, pinkish, sea-encrusted jug and started down the gangplank. The people were pushing and pulling, getting off the boat, coming on board, and he shouted as they shouted. He came to the quay, and another porter, stumbling on a mooring rope, fell against him and he dropped the amphora.

Two thousand years went down in a dusty sound of earth falling. Well.

Ten years before there were still amphorae and other relics of the Greeks and Phœnicians and Romans in the shallow coves of the islands of Ibiza, but now there were mostly only almost valueless objects of more recent times; valuable specimens were very rare. The American had paid $500 for this water jug of a Phœnician sailor, having had it verified as authentic by the authorities. Naturally he was angry.

But he was also a sensible man and knew that never in a lifetime could the porter Vicente make $500, so he was resigned and ready to forget his loss.

Not so Vicente. He knew the value men set now on these useless old jugs and pots; he had seen the disappointment on the face of the American. Vicente was an honorable man and he wanted to make amends.

He followed the American to his hotel, pleaded for his name and address, and promised to pay him back. A ragged piece of paper torn from a diary and scribbled with Abraham Lincoln Smith, 72 Hudson Avenue, Milwaukee, Wisconsin, U.S.A. became his most valuable possession. It was to him the ultimate milepost on the long road of his search.

I believe that somehow, in his dreams, Vicente saw himself at last arriving in Milwaukee, Wisconsin, U.S.A., with the ancient Phœnician amphora under his arm, receiving with joy the praise that would greet him there.

Vicente knew that he would never have the money to buy an amphora, but what was to prevent his finding one? Others had, dozens of them in the time of his boyhood. Why not he?

He had no family, so it did not take him long to bid farewell to his life in Barcelona, that bustling, busy city by the sea, where he had carried bags for the price of a small glass of wine in a smoky wineshop, and a windowless room to roof his nights.

When he had sold his few possessions he had the deck fare to Ibiza, and a little more. From the stern of the boat he looked back and saw the city sink into the sea, and for the first time he knew that his years there had been a prison of his own making. He had never, there, lifted up his eyes from the narrow streets to the wide sky.

*And once again, as when he was a boy, the sea sang to him.*

Back on the islands he set about the task he had chosen. He learned where the last amphora had been found, and he realized, as had others before him, that since the ancient pieces were valuable, all the inshore places must have been searched and emptied of their treasure.

Young Sandik, of Santa Eulalia del Rio, the carpenter's son, had made himself a reputation as an undersea swimmer. He had found a cannon at the bottom of the sea—but that's another story. To consult him, Vicente travelled by bus to Santa Eulalia del Rio, and Sandik's advice was brief. Get a mask, get flippers, go far out into the sea. There, way out, were still unknown shallows, no deeper than the height of a man, or twice or thrice the height of a man, and caught in the caves of the sea bottom, treasures might still be.

Now Vicente, like many of the island-born, had never learned to swim. But he spent the rest of his money, as Sandik advised, on a good snorkel and flippers and a mask. Then he took the little mail boat *Manolito* back to his island of Formentera. There, camping on the beach, scrounging his meals, intent as are all men with a singleness of purpose to urge them on, he set about teaching himself to swim.

He was over 60 then. An old man, as time makes men like Vicente old. Yet he was young in his urgency to learn and go on toward the far horizon of his purpose.

He learned to swim, and he learned to dive with the snorkel and the flippers and the mask, a froglike, crablike figure in the clear shallows about the beaches of Cala Pujol. He ventured farther and farther, to where the water turned purple, where the deeps began. This was the most talkative time of his life, after his first dives, for he could not contain his wonder at the unexpected beauty of the deep sea. The gardens of starfish, the varicolored, bug-eyed gentle fish that followed him, the slant of translucent sunlight on the mysterious caves and rocks—these he recounted to the fishermen who toiled upon the surface of the sea. And his tales were touched with wonder and awe. Never, he swore, had he known such freedom as at the bottom of the sea.

"But you can't breathe there!"

"One breathes with one's eyes, one's pores."

Never had he heard such music.

"But there is only silence under the sea?"

"It is a singing silence. Like many instruments sending their purest sounds up to the sky."

*There is that to the Spanish language. The plowman often speaks the language of poetry. It is the way the words arrange themselves.*

Day by day, week by week, month by month, and so into the years, Vicente, searching for the amphora which in honor he felt he must find to replace the one he had broken, grew happier. Each day was a new delight, a new adventure. No longer were his days imprisoned by the needs of the hours. Somehow there was always something for those needs, a fish to grill, a glass of wine, a piece of bread, a box of matches. To the fishermen his search had become a part of their life on the beach and the sea, and their generosity was quick, unthinking.

They told me the story of Vicente, that day the wind blew from Africa and stirred up the depths of the sea and sent the high green waves scurrying, and I, too, searched the horizon for the little boat. Then I turned to Father Pedro, the curé of San Fernando, who had joined us.

"What do you think, Father?" I said. "Will old Vicente find his amphora?"

The fat little priest joined his fingers. His eyes, too, were on the horizon, but he seemed undisturbed. The wind from Africa swayed the bamboo shelter over us.

"Well, now, you see," he said, "Vicente has the search. It is not what one finds, you know, but the search itself that is important. Only the search."

Last year, on another day, when the sea rose suddenly, stirred to tumult by the wind, the little boat Vicente had borrowed was tossed back to the beach.

No one saw the old man again.

The seas had been heavy.

But tied, securely, wrapped in seaweed at the bottom of the boat, was an amphora, an ancient Phœnician vessel salvaged from the centuries and the sea.

Father Pedro and the fishermen who had been Vicente's friends asked me, since I knew English, to write to Abraham Lincoln Smith of Milwaukee, Wisconsin, U.S.A. I did. I wrote a number of times to the address we had and finally to the mayor of the city.

No one had heard of him.

Annoyed by the foolish old man who had dropped his souvenir, the American had fabricated a name to get rid of him. Perhaps, however, he did come from Milwaukee. We do not know.

**Eva-Lis Wuorio** was born in 1918 in Finland, and immigrated to Canada at the age of 11. Her works include *To Fight in Silence, Escape If You Can, The Land of Right Up and Down,* and *The Woman With the Portuguese.* A number of her books have a World War II setting.

## 1. *Response*

    **a.** Create a list of adjectives that the narrator would (or did) use to capture Vicente's character. Was Vicente appealing or interesting to you? Why or why not?

    **b.** In your view, how plausible is Vicente's decision to devote his life to finding a replacement for the amphora he broke? Explain.

    **c.** Reread the final seven paragraphs of the story. What ideas do you think the author is communicating in these concluding passages?

    **d.** What is your personal response to "The Singing Silence"? Comment both on the theme of the story and also on the way the theme is presented.

## 2. *Vocabulary* Context Cues

Make a list of any unfamiliar words and expressions you encountered while reading the story. Were you able to infer their meaning from the context in which they were placed? Do you think the author anticipated some of the difficulties readers might face? Explain.

## 3. *Writing* Eulogy

Using details and quotations from the story, write a **eulogy** for Vicente. Once you have revised your work, rehearse presenting the eulogy in front of a small group. What suggestions can the group make for improving the eulogy?

A **eulogy** is a tribute to someone who has just died, and is often delivered as a speech at a funeral.

## 4. *Media* Inspirational Message

"The Singing Silence" offers an inspirational message on the importance of dreams and goals in life. Employing a medium other than writing, create a representation of the theme of the story. Your work should make a statement that Vicente would agree with. Your representation might take the form of a musical composition, video, digital image, poster, dance, dramatization, or collage.

# *Poetry*

Poetry is life distilled.

*Gwendolyn Brooks*

# { Poets on Poetry

How can we as readers get the most out of poetry? William Shakespeare advises us to see poetry "feelingly."

Here is what some other poets say about poetry. Would you agree? What would you add?

"Poetry gives your most intimate self
the chance to talk to the most intimate
self of another. When these two meet
the sparks fly, the poem is charged with
light, and a new way of seeing and saying
enters the world."
—Lorna Crozier

"Literature is a state of culture,
poetry is a state of grace."
—Juan Ramon Jimenez

"Poetry is to prose
as dancing is to walking."
—John Wain

"If I read a book [and] it makes my whole body so
cold no fire ever can warm me I know that is poetry.
If I feel physically as if the top of my head were taken
off, I know that is poetry."
—Emily Dickinson

"To read a poem is to hear it with our eyes;
to hear it is to see it with our ears."
—Octavio Paz

"Poetry is a string of words that parades
without a permit."
—Linda Hogan

Previous Page:
*Rock Painting. Prehistoric Art, Zimbabwe*

# A Poet's Advice to Students

By E.E. Cummings

A poet is somebody who feels, and who expresses his feeling through words.

This may sound easy. It isn't.

A lot of people think or believe or know they feel—but that's thinking or believing or knowing; not feeling. And poetry is feeling—not knowing or believing or thinking.

Almost anybody can learn to think or believe or know, but not a single human being can be taught to feel. Why? Because whenever you think or you believe or you know, you're a lot of other people: but the moment you feel, you're nobody-but-yourself.

To be nobody-but-yourself—in a world which is doing its best, night and day, to make you everybody else—means to fight the hardest battle which any human being can fight; and never stop fighting.

As for expressing nobody-but-yourself in words, that means working just a little harder than anybody who isn't a poet can possibly imagine. Why? Because nothing is quite as easy as using words like somebody else. We all of us do exactly this nearly all of the time—and whenever we do it, we're not poets.

If, at the end of your first ten or fifteen years of fighting and working and feeling, you find you've written one line of one poem, you'll be very lucky indeed.

And so my advice to all young people who wish to become poets is: do something easy, like learning how to blow up the world—unless you're not only willing, but glad, to feel and work and fight till you die.

Does this sound dismal? It isn't.

It's the most wonderful life on earth.

Or so I feel.

# I Carried With Me Poems

By Gail Dusenbery

I carried with me poems, poems which spewed out of
    everything:  I saw poems hanging from the clotheslines,
    hanging from the streetlamps:  I saw poems glowing
    in the bushes, pushing out of the earth as tulips do;
I felt poems breathe in the dark March night like ghosts
    which squared and wheeled through the air;
I felt poems brushing the tops of chimneys, brushing
    by in the dark;  I felt poems being born in the city,
    Venuses breaking through a shattered sea of mirrors;
I felt all the poets of the city straining,
    isolated poets, knowing none of the others, straining;
I felt that some gazed into the March night, looking,
    and finding;
and others were running down the steep streets,
    seeking, and seeking to embrace;
and others stood in empty bookstores turning over pages
    of fellow poets whom they loved but didn't know;
and some pondered over coffee growing cold, in harshly
    lit cafeterias, and gazed at the reflections of the eaters
    in the wall-to-wall mirrors:
some dwelt on what it was to grow old;
some dwelled on love;
some had gone out of time;
some, going out of time, looked back into time, and
    started;
I felt all these lives and existences, all with poems at
    their center;

I knew none of these poets;
but I felt these intimations augured well, for me, and
    for poetry:
and my steps grew big, giant steps, I bounded down
    Park Street,
a tall, taciturn, fast-walking poets' accomplice.

# Poetry Is . . .

By Betty Lies

Poetry is music, the tempos and tones of life, the beat of language enacted. It is the human voice singing its joys and griefs. It is movement. It is voice-dance.

Poetry is language, its deepest structures, grammar, syntax, etymologies, the origins of thought. It is metaphor and the rhythms of persuasion. It is precision and concision.

Poetry is pictures painted with words.

Poetry is seeing, noticing, close-ups of nature and its creatures. It's looking at the universe, the immense and the microscopic.

Poetry is a bridge between reason and the emotions; it helps us think and validates feeling. It calls to the imagination and demands an answer.

Poetry is the collective memory of the human race, the record of our experience through the ages. It gives flesh to dates and eras, and tells the lived reality of wars, cultural events, historical movements.

Poetry begins to ask the questions for our necessary spiritual quest.

Poetry is the universal voice, the human spirit calling across boundaries of time, geography, culture, age, race, gender, experience. Through it we learn about the other, and about ourselves.

We read and write poems and discover that we are not alone.

# I Wrote a Poem

By Jennifer Takyi

I wrote a poem,
And nobody liked it,
So I threw it away,
But it won't let me go,
It's part of me.

# What You Are Doing Now

By Gary Hyland

In grade eleven
you and this poem
meet for the first time
in an English classroom
when you would rather be
almost anywhere else
    gazing      lazing
    dancing   snoozing
    kissing    cruising
10   but all of history
from Cro-Magnon clans
to Puritans
to the Department of Education
was mobilized to get you
and this poem here/now

and you're thinking     *hey*
*not so bad so far*     *hey*
*I understand most of this*
*At least it's not that gloopy*
20   *antique tombstone stuff/not*

    O spirit soft of summer's breezes
    Who dwelleth in yon western reaches
    Where gulls conspire to form friezes
    With white waves on craggy beaches

*at least it's not that snarly*
*strung-out lumpy stuff/not*

my snow

stems

roses

30      till they

(petal

me)

*Hey this is like football*
*he pins*                    *I boot*
*Hey it's basketball*
*he passes*                  *I shoot*
*Manoman I can do it!*
*Hey there's nothing to it!*

Then your teacher announces
40   that you have thirty minutes
to write an analysis
of this poem
                    and when you look
the poem spits in your face
and stops.


# How Beautifully Useless

By Raymond Souster

How beautifully useless,
how deliciously defiant
a poem is!

### 1. Response

**a.** Both Jennifer Takyi and Raymond Souster use few words to convey many meanings. Take either "I Wrote a Poem" or "How Beautifully Useless" and expand upon what you think the author is suggesting about the nature of poetry.

**b.** Discuss what E.E. Cummings and Gail Dusenbery are saying about poetry, poets, and readers. Which sentiments or ideas do you agree with most? Which do you disagree with? Are there statements that you find difficult to understand? Suggest possible meanings for those statements. Summarize your conclusions for the class.

**c.** Select one statement from "Poetry Is . . ." by Betty Lies and find a poem that you think exemplifies the statement. Explain your choice.

**d.** Express your own view of poetry in a brief opinion piece. Try to support your opinion by referring to specific poems or personal experiences with poetry.

### 2. Oral Language *Dramatic Reading*

Prepare a dramatized oral reading of "What You Are Doing Now." In a paragraph or two, describe the techniques you employed to make your reading more effective.

### 3. Writing *Poetry*

Write your own version of "I Carried With Me Poems," starting with the same first line: "I carried with me poems, poems which spewed out of everything." Use images and details from your own experience or knowledge base.

### 4. Language Conventions *Run-on Sentences*

As you read poetry you will notice that some poets use grammar or punctuation in unconventional ways for a particular effect. For example, in "I Wrote a Poem" on page 167, Takyi constructs a five-line poem using one run-on sentence. Think about the effect these lines would have if she had used end punctuation. Reread the other poems in this section, looking for run-on sentences. How have the poets used run-on sentences effectively?

# Lyric Poetry

One way of classifying a poem is by the function it serves. A lyric poem is a poem whose primary function is to express a state of mind or a powerful emotion. The term *lyric* comes from *lyre*, a musical instrument similar to a harp. In ancient Greece, poets recited their verse to the accompaniment of music played on the lyre.

Lyric poetry can be intensely personal and is often written in the first person. Many popular forms, such as free verse and haiku, can be classified by their function as lyric poetry.

A lyric poem not only expresses emotion, it evokes emotion in the reader. Identify the powerful emotions expressed in each of the following short lyric poems. Which of the poems do you find most evocative? Explain your choice.

*After a Heated Argument*
By Kaneto Tota
*Translated from the Japanese by Makoto Ueda*

After a heated argument
I go out to the street
and become a motorcycle.

*Love Is*
By Ann Darr

    a flock of birds, soaring, twisting, turning,
floating, lifting, swooping, landing, splitting into
pieces (individual birds) that can peck peck peck
before they once again unite in the flock that, rising,
goes reeling, shifting, flying (flying, that's the word
I was looking for) right out of sight.

# Calgary 2 am

By Christopher Wiseman

In spite of the fact that it is twenty below
and the winter has lasted six months

in spite of being starved    starved almost to death
for greenness and warmth   flowers and birds

in spite of the deadness of endless classrooms
shopping centres    television programmes

in spite of the pains in the gut    the migraines
the wakings    the palpitations

in spite of the sickening knowledge of laziness
of failure to meet obligations

in spite of all these things    and more
I have to report that the moon tonight

is filling the house with a wild blueness
my children grow    excel    are healthy

my wife is gentle    there are friends
and once in a while a poem will come

In spite of the fact that it is twenty below
tonight I smile    Summer bursts inside me

10

# Life in Our Village

By Matei Markwei

In our little village
When elders are around
Boys must not look at girls
And girls must not look at boys
Because the elders say
That is not good.

Even when night comes
Boys must play separately
Girls must play separately
10  But humanity is weak
So boys and girls meet.

The boys play hide and seek
And the girls play hide and seek.
The boys know where the girls hide
And the girls know where the boys hide
So in their hide and seek
Boys seek girls
Girls seek boys
And each to each sing
20  Songs of love.

# God's World

By Edna St. Vincent Millay

O world, I cannot hold thee close enough!
   Thy winds, thy wide grey skies!
   Thy mists, that roll and rise!
Thy woods, this autumn day, that ache and sag
And all but cry with colour! That gaunt crag
To crush! To lift the lean of that black bluff!
World, World, I cannot get thee close enough!

Long have I known a glory in it all,
      But never knew I this:
      Here such a passion is
As stretcheth me apart,—Lord, I do fear
Thou'st made the world too beautiful this year;
My soul is all but out of me,—let fall
No burning leaf; prithee, let no bird call.

10

*Spring Wind — Apollo Coast* by Paul Grignon

Examine this image and discuss its use of colour, texture, space, light, and depth. How do these contribute to its mood? How does this painting affect the viewer?

# A Red, Red Rose

By Robert Burns

O, my luve's like a red, red rose
That's newly sprung in June.
O, my luve is like the melodie
That's sweetly played in tune.

As fair art thou, my bonnie lass,
So deep in luve am I;
And I will luve thee still, my dear,
Till a' the seas gang dry.                          **gang:** go

Till a' the seas gang dry, my dear,
10  And the rocks melt wi' the sun;
And I will luve thee still, my dear,
While the sands o' life shall run.

And fare thee weel, my only luve,                   **weel:** well
And fare thee weel a while!
And I will come again, my luve,
Though it were ten thousand mile.

# Canadian Sunrise

By Joan Besen of Prairie Oyster

Well, tired, bone-weary
Can't stand another day of rain
Go shout your troubles to the mountains
But the mountains echo back
It's the same old chain

**Chorus:**
Crying give me a sign, give me a sign.
However rough the road, however dark the skies,
Your frozen soul will melt like April ice
When a shot of gold hits your eyes.
10   Canadian sunrise, woa Canadian sunrise, woa.

Even smoking, dust choking.
When's it gonna rain again?
You had big dreams, now they've all gone flat.
Blown away to nothin' by the prairie rain.

**Chorus**

Between the rock and the raging sea,
Running till you're ragged and tossed.
Searching for something you think you'll never find
And you find out it was never lost.

**Chorus**

# *Demasduit's Dream*

By Bob Hallett of Great Big Sea

I dreamt I saw a woman
Standing by the strand
Waiting for her people
To come in from the land

Waiting there for seven days
She built a fire in the sand
Waiting for her people
To come in from the land

"Demasduit's Dream" tells the story of a Beothuk woman, Demasduit (also known as Mary March).
She was captured in March of 1819 by the English, at Red Indian Lake, Newfoundland and Labrador.
Her husband, chief Nonosabasut, tried to rescue her, and was killed. She remained with her captives,
learning English quickly, and provided them with a better understanding of her language.

She had the look of a refugee
10     Hiding in her eyes
And when I tried to talk to her
She answered with a cry

And pointed to the water
Out beyond the harbour line
Where a thousand ships lay waiting
They lay waiting for my sign
But . . .

**Chorus:**
I remember days of sunlight
With my father by my side
20     And the children, ran before us
Like the foam upon the tide

We ran like frightened partridge
When the strangers came to talk
Bringing sickness 'round them
And the thunder in their walk

We ran into the valleys
And we ran into the hills
They only ran before us,
Driven by the strangers' will

**Chorus**

30     I'm waiting by the landwash
Giant standing near
I see them coming always
Children in their fear

I'm waiting on my blanket
And the giant waits with me
And I will wait here always
As they fill the endless sea

**Chorus**

# As in the Beginning

By Mary di Michele

A man has two hands and when one
gets caught on the belt and his fingers
are amputated and then patched
he cannot work. His hands are insured
however so he gets some money
for the work his hands have done before.
If he loses a finger he gets a flat sum
of $250 for each digit &/or $100 for a joint
missing for the rest of his stay on earth,
10  like an empty stool at a beggar's banquet.
When the hands are my father's hands
it makes me cry although my pen must keep scratching
its head across the page of another night.
To you my father is a stranger
and perhaps you think the insurance paid is enough.

Give me my father's hands when they are not broken
and swollen,
give me my father's hands, young again,
and holding the hands of my mother,
20  give me my father's hands still brown and uncallused,
beautiful hands that broke bread for us at table,
hands as smooth as marble and naked as the morning,
give me hands without a number tattooed at the wrist,
without the copper sweat of clinging change,
give my father's hands as they were in the beginning,
whole,
open,
warm
and without fear.

# Do Not Stand at My Grave and Weep

By Mary E. Frye

Do not stand at my grave and weep.
I am not there, I do not sleep.
I am a thousand winds that blow,
I am the diamond glints on snow,
I am the sunlight on ripened grain,
I am the gentle autumn rain.
When you awaken in the morning's hush
I am the swift uplifting rush
Of quiet birds in circled flight.
I am the soft stars that shine at night.
Do not stand at my grave and cry,
I am not there. I did not die.

## 1. Response

**a.** For each poem in this section, write a brief phrase that sums up the emotion or state of mind the poet is expressing.

**b.** Which poem did you like best? Why?

**c.** The poems in this section have varying degrees of poetic structure, from the free verse of "As in the Beginning," to the patterned rhythm and rhyme of "God's World." What advantages and disadvantages come with a high degree of poetic structure? With less structure?

**d.** "Do Not Stand at My Grave and Weep" has become a favoured reading at funeral and memorial ceremonies. What do you think accounts for its popularity?

**e.** Write your own lyric poem. Choose an emotion or state of mind that is not represented by the poems in this section.

2. *Literature Studies* *Style* The style of "Life in Our Village" and "As in the Beginning" could be described as *understated*. In a group, explore the meaning of the term *understated*. What might be some characteristics of an understated style? Discuss whether "Life in Our Village" and "As in the Beginning" would be effective if the feelings expressed were more explicitly projected.

3. *Critical Thinking* Here is what Joan Besen says about her song "Canadian Sunrise": "I was trying to be descriptive about Canada, from one end to the other, trying to capture the experience of going back and forth across the country so much, as we do. In Canada you go to extremes: you go from ocean to mountain to rain forest and then it's absolutely flat as though the previous extreme never existed. Then it's rocks and trees for miles until you hit another ocean. If you go back and forth you really notice it." In a group, use Besen's statement to help you interpret "Canadian Sunrise." Make connections between the statement and specific lines in the song. If you wrote a song about Canada, what emotion would you want to express?

4. *Media* *Collage* Create a collage of visuals and text that evokes the feelings of a lyric poem of your choice. Your collage can be any combination of visuals, lines from the poem, and your own words.

5. *Language Conventions* *Parallel Structure* In the poem "As in the Beginning," the poet, Mary di Michele, has used **parallel structure**, with the repetition of the phrase "Give me my father's hands ..." Which other poets have used parallel structure in this section? Why do you think poets would choose to use this device?

**Parallel structure** is the repeated use of the same phrase or sentence, or the repeated use of a similar sentence structure. Parallel structure can be used to create balance or place emphasis on certain lines.

Painting was called silent poetry
and poetry speaking painting.
—*Ralph Waldo Emerson.*

# Sonnet

The *sonnet* is a form of poetry that traditionally follows strict rules of metre, rhyme, structure, and length. It has fourteen lines, ten syllables per line, and a formal rhyme scheme. Most sonnets can also be classified as *lyric poems*.

Poets continue to be attracted to the creative challenge posed by the sonnet form. The best poets are able to fill the small and highly structured space of a sonnet with deep emotion and profound meaning.

Below is Elizabeth Barrett Browning's famous love poem, "How Do I Love Thee?" Speculate on why this sonnet gained the status of a classic. Do you think it still speaks to readers today?

*Sonnet XLII*
By Elizabeth Barrett Browning

How do I love thee? Let me count the ways.
I love thee to the depth and breadth and height
My soul can reach, when feeling out of sight
For the ends of Being and ideal Grace.
I love thee to the level of every day's
Most quiet need, by sun and candlelight.
I love thee freely, as men strive for Right;
I love thee purely, as they turn from Praise.
I love thee with the passion put to use
In my old griefs, and with my childhood's faith;
I love thee with a love I seemed to lose
With my lost saints,—I love thee with the breath,
Smiles, tears, of all my life!—and, if God choose,
I shall but love thee better after death.

# Composed Upon Westminster Bridge

By William Wordsworth

Earth has not anything to show more fair:
Dull would he be of soul who could pass by
A sight so touching in its majesty:
This City now doth, like a garment wear
The beauty of the morning; silent, bare,
Ships, towers, domes, theatres, and temples lie
Open unto the fields, and to the sky;
All bright and glittering in the smokeless air.
Never did sun more beautifully steep
In his first splendour valley, rock, or hill;
Ne'er saw I, never felt, a calm so deep!
The river glideth at his own sweet will:
Dear God! the very houses seem asleep;
And all that mighty heart is lying still!


# In the Crowd

By Ethelwyn Wertherald

Here in the crowded city's busy street,
Swayed by the eager, jostling, hasting throng,
Where Traffic's voice grows harsher and more strong,
I see within the stream of hurrying feet
A company of trees in their retreat,
Dew-bathed, dream-wrapped, and with a thrush's song
Emparadizing all the place, along
Whose paths I hear the pulse of Beauty beat.
'Twas yesterday I walked beneath the trees,
To-day I tread the city's stony ways;
And still the spell that o'er my spirit came
Turns harshest sounds to shy bird ecstasies,
Pours scent of pine through murky chimney haze,
And gives each careworn face a woodland frame.

# Sonnet LV

By William Shakespeare

Not marble, nor the gilded monuments
Of princes, shall outlive this powerful rhyme;
But you shall shine more bright in these contents
Than unswept stone besmear'd with sluttish time.
When wasteful war shall statues overturn,
And broils root out the work of masonry,
Nor Mars his sword nor war's quick fire shall burn
The living record of your memory.
'Gainst death and all-oblivious enmity
Shall you pace forth; your praise shall still find room
Even in the eyes of all posterity
That wear this world out to the ending doom.
    So, till the judgment that yourself arise,
    You live in this, and dwell in lover's eyes.

# "Not only marble, but the plastic toys"

By Wendy Cope

Not only marble, but the plastic toys
From cornflake packets will outlive this rhyme:
I can't immortalize you, love—our joys
Will lie unnoticed in the vault of time.
When Mrs Thatcher has been cast in bronze
And her administration is a page
In some O-level text-book, when the dons
Have analysed the story of our age,
When travel firms sell tours of outer space
And aeroplanes take off without a sound
And Tulse Hill has become a trendy place
And Upper Norwood's on the underground
Your beauty and my name will be forgotten—
My love is true, but all my verse is rotten.

**Mrs Thatcher:** Margaret Thatcher, former Prime Minister of the U.K.

**O-level:** General high school level in the U.K.

**dons:** professors

**Tulse Hill, Upper Norwood:** suburbs of London

# Ozymandias

## By Percy Bysshe Shelley

I met a traveller from an antique land
Who said: Two vast and trunkless legs of stone
Stand in the desert ... Near them, on the sand,
Half sunk, a shattered visage lies, whose frown,
And wrinkled lip, and sneer of cold command,
Tell that its sculptor well those passions read
Which yet survive, stamped on these lifeless things,
The hand that mock'd them and the heart that fed:
And on the pedestal these words appear:
'My name is Ozymandias, king of kings:
Look on my works, ye Mighty, and despair!'
Nothing beside remains. Round the decay
Of that colossal wreck, boundless and bare
The lone and level sands stretch far away.

## 1. Response

**a.** Several of the sonnets pose a challenge because they were written long ago, and the way English is spoken and written has changed since then. In a group, discuss how you responded to this challenge. Identify five reading strategies that contemporary readers can use to help them better understand poetry written in older varieties of English.

**b.** There are many sonnets that speculate on which endures longest—material objects or intangibles such as love or power. Shakespeare's "Sonnet LV," Cope's "Not only marble...," and Shelley's "Ozymandias" explore this question. In groups, analyse one of these sonnets. Come to a consensus on three statements that describe the position your poem is taking on the question described above. Write your sentences on poster paper and display them in your classroom.

**c.** Wordsworth's "Composed Upon Westminster Bridge" and Wertherald's "In the Crowd" look at the urban environment in unconventional ways. How are the poets' views similar and different? Did you prefer one poem over the other? Explain. What is your own perspective on city life?

2. **Literature Studies** *Sonnet Types* Carefully study the metre, rhyme scheme, and organization of Browning's Petrarchan sonnet ("Sonnet XLII") and Shakespeare's English sonnet ("Sonnet LV"). What are the distinguishing characteristics of each? Report your findings in a chart of your own design. When your chart is complete, use literary glossaries in the library or on the Internet to learn about the differences between the two forms of sonnet.

3. **Writing** *Parody* Wendy Cope's "Not only marble . . . " is a *parody* (a humorous imitation) of Shakespeare's "Sonnet LV." What specific features of Shakespeare's poem has Cope imitated? Are the messages of the poems similar or different? Select a serious poem and write your own parody of it.

4. **Oral Language** *In Conversation* Reread these sonnets, noting how the poets have used a first-person speaker. Each poem seems to be addressing a specific person, delivering a message using poetic language and structure. Use plain, non-poetic language to recreate one of these poems. Deliver your version to others.

The best and most beautiful things in the world cannot be seen or even touched.
They must be felt with the heart.

*—Helen Keller.*

# { Light Verse

Light verse is the comedian of the poetic world. Its intention is to be humorous, clever, and sometimes rude. Though light verse often offers perceptive observations about human foibles and follies, there is always a whimsical or playful tone. More than anything, poets who indulge in light verse love to play and to pun with language.

Do you think these poems are clever? If so, how are they clever? How have the poets played with words?

*The Limerick*
Anonymous

The limerick packs laughs anatomical
Into space that is quite economical,
But the good ones, I've seen
So seldom are clean,
And the clean ones so seldom are comical.

*To Make a Prairie*
By Emily Dickinson

To make a prairie it takes a clover and one bee,
One clover, and a bee,
And revery.
The revery alone will do,
If bees are few.

*World's Shortest Pessimistic Poem*
By Robert Zend

Hope?
Nope.

*Christmas Gift*
By Victor Howes

Cashmere is a sweater
Mere cash, even better.

# Writer's Block in the Computer Age

By Peggy Smith Krachun

Cursor, cursor, blinking cursor
Shade of iridescent green
Cursor in the "Home" position
On my new computer screen

Cursor at the starting gate
Chomping at the bit and byte
Pawing at the screen, impatient
Nagging me to start to write

Cursor poised for the race
10   In Position One, Line One
Waiting for a brilliant word
To set off the starting gun

Until now a plain old scribbler
Was the only thing I'd use
On it I would draw and doodle
While I waited for the Muse

Now I have a winking cursor
Mocking me in brilliant green
Have you ever tried to doodle
20   On a blank computer screen?

Nagging cursor, cursed cursor
Blinking on without a sound
Go away until I'm ready
I'll never write with you around.

# from *Spellbound*

I have a spelling checker
It came with my PC;
It plainly marks four my revue
Mistakes I cannot sea.
I've run this poem threw it,
I'm sure your pleased too no,
Its letter perfect in it's weigh,
My checker tolled me sew.

# *A Spider Danced a Cosy Jig*

By Irving Layton

A spider danced a cosy jig
Upon a frail trapeze;
And from a far-off clover field
An ant was heard to sneeze.

And kings that day were wise and just,
And stones began to bleed;
A dead man rose to tell a tale,
A bigot changed his creed.

The stableboy forgot his pride,
10    The queen confessed an itch;
And lo! more wonderful than all,
The poor man blessed the rich.

**188** • Light Verse

# *Crazy Times*

By Miriam Waddington

When the birds riot
and the airplanes walk,
when the busy sit,
and the silent talk;

When the rains blow
and the winds pour,
when the sky is a land
and the sea its shore,

10    When shells grow snails
and worms eat toads,
when winters chase summers
on upside-down roads,

We'll sit by our fires
and warm our hands,
and tell old tales
of bygone lands.

# *Kidnap Poem*

By Nikki Giovanni

ever been kidnapped
by a poet
if i were a poet
i'd kidnap you

put you in my phrases
and meter you to jones beach
or maybe coney island
or maybe just to my house

lyric you in lilacs
10 dash you in the rain
alliterate the beach
to complement my sea

play the lyre for you
ode you with my love song
anything to win you
wrap you in the red Black green
show you off to mama

yeah if i were
a poet i'd kid
20 nap you

## from *Very Like a Whale*

By Ogden Nash

One thing that literature would be greatly the better
    for
Would be a more restricted employment by authors
    of simile and metaphor.
Authors of all races, be they Greeks, Romans, Teutons
    or Celts,
Can't seem just to say that anything is the thing it is
    but have to go out of their way to say that it is
    like something else....

10 That's the kind of thing that's being done all the time
    by poets, from Homer to Tennyson;
They're always comparing ladies to lilies and veal to
    venison,
And they always say things like that the snow is a white
    blanket after a winter storm.

Oh it is, is it, all right then, you sleep under a six-inch
blanket of snow and I'll sleep under a half-inch
blanket of unpoetical blanket material and we'll
see which one keeps warm,
20 And after that maybe you'll begin to comprehend
dimly
What I mean by too much metaphor and simile.

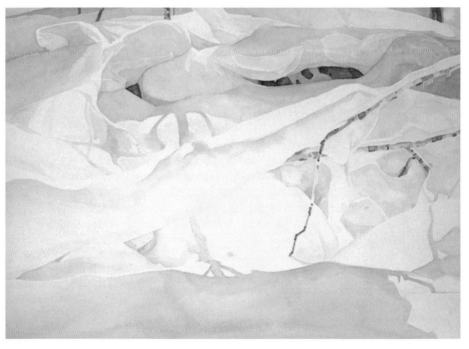

*Winter's Blanket #1* by David McEown, watercolour

In your notebook, write a paragraph describing this painting.
Try to make your description vivid without using similes
or metaphors.

Poetry is the impish attempt
to paint the colour of the wind.
—*Maxwell Bodenheim*

1. *Response*
   a. "Writer's Block in the Computer Age" and "Spellbound" both deal humorously with the effect of computers on the writing process. Explain the techniques the poets use to generate the humour. Underneath their playful tone, these poems convey serious messages. What are they?
   b. What do "A Spider Danced a Cosy Jig" and "Crazy Times" have in common? Which poem do you prefer? Why? Write an additional stanza or two for either (or both) of the poems.
   c. Identify five specific examples of wordplay in "Kidnap Poem" and describe how the poet is playing with language in each case. Do you ever use wordplay in your own writing or speech? Explain.

2. *Language Conventions* *Spelling* Rewrite "Spellbound" making all the necessary corrections. On a different sheet of paper, write an additional two stanzas in the error-filled style of the original. Challenge a classmate to find and correct the errors. What type of error has the spell checker missed? How do you check for those types of errors in your own writing?

3. *Writing* *Limericks* Most limericks, like the one on page 186, are written to amuse, and many are written about interesting individuals—real or invented. For example:

   > Limerick
   > (Author unknown)
   >
   > There was a young woman named Bright
   > Whose speed was much faster than light.
   > She set out one day
   > In a relative way,
   > And returned on the previous night.

   Conventional limericks are five lines long and follow a definite pattern: lines one, two, and five contain eight syllables, and lines three and four contain six. The rhyme scheme is *aabba*. Write several limericks about the characters in a book you have studied or in a famous TV show or movie.

# Satirical Poetry

Sometimes humour is used for the serious purpose of effecting positive change in people or in society. That kind of writing is known as *satire*. Poets were the first satirists, and the tradition of satirical poetry is alive and well today.

To fully appreciate satire, we must identify who or what is being ridiculed. Is it a specific person or society in general? Is it a behaviour, a belief, an attitude, or merely a minor human failing or weakness? All are legitimate targets for the satirical poet's wit.

In these poems, identify what exactly is being ridiculed. Discuss whether the attack or criticism is justified. What positive changes in attitude or behaviour do you think the poet is attempting to initiate?

*Earth*
By John Hall Wheelock

"A planet doesn't explode of itself," said drily
The Martian astronomer, gazing off into the air—
"That they were able to do it is proof that highly
Intelligent beings must have been living there."

*Green Memory*
By Langston Hughes

A wonderful time—the War:
when money rolled in
and blood rolled out.

But blood
was far away
from here—

Money was near.

# St. George

## By Nancy Senior

My dragon always loved walks
He used to go to the wall
where the golden chain hung
and take it in his mouth
laying his head on my lap
sideways, so the fire wouldn't burn my skirt

He looked so funny that way
with his legs dragging the floor
and his rear end high up
10 because he couldn't bend his hind legs
He was so well trained
always keeping his claws retracted
when he walked on the rug

With him on the leash, I could go anywhere
No band of robbers dared attack

This morning in the woods
we had stopped for a drink
where a spring gushes out of a cave

when suddenly, a man in armour
20 riding a white horse
leapt out of the bushes
crying "Have no fear, Maiden
I will save you"

And before I could say a word
he had stabbed my dragon in the throat
and leaping down from the horse
cut off his head
and held it up for me to see
the poor dead eyes still surprised
30 and mine filling with tears
He hadn't even had time to put out his claws

And the man said
"Don't cry, Maiden
You are safe now
But let me give you some good advice
Don't ever walk alone in the woods
for the next time you meet a dragon
there might not be a knight around to save you"

*St. George and the Dragon* by Uccello (Paolo di Dono), 1460. Oil on canvas

Nancy Senior, the author of "St. George," was inspired by this painting to write her poem. Would you interpret this painting in the same way? Explain.

# The Unknown Citizen

By W. H. Auden

(To JS/07/M/378
This Marble Monument
Is Erected by the State)

He was found by the Bureau of Statistics to be
One against whom there was no official complaint,
And all the reports on his conduct agree
That, in the modern sense of an old-fashioned word, he was a saint,
For in everything he did he served the Greater Community.
Except for the War till the day he retired
10    He worked in a factory and never got fired,
But satisfied his employers, Fudge Motors Inc.
Yet he wasn't a scab or odd in his views,
For his Union reports that he paid his dues,
(Our report on his Union shows it was sound)
And our Social Psychology workers found
That he was popular with his mates and liked a drink.
The Press are convinced that he bought a paper every day
And that his reactions to advertisements were normal in every way.
Policies taken out in his name prove that he was fully insured,
20    And his Health-card shows he was once in hospital but left it cured.
Both Producers Research and High-Grade Living declare
He was fully sensible to the advantages of the Installment Plan
And had everything necessary to the Modern Man,
A phonograph, a radio, a car and a frigidaire.
Our researchers into Public Opinion are content
That he held the proper opinions for the time of year;
When there was peace, he was for peace; when there was war, he
       went.
He was married and added five children to the population,
30    Which our Eugenist says was the right number for a parent of his
       generation,
And our teachers report that he never interfered with their education.
Was he free? Was he happy? The question is absurd:
Had anything been wrong, we should certainly have heard.

# #9

By Lawrence Ferlinghetti

'History is made
    of the lies of the victors'
        but you would never dream it
            from the covers of the textbooks
                nor from the way the victors are portrayed
                as super-benevolent altruists
                    and lovers of the poor and downtrodden
                who never had a chance to
                    rise up and write their own dubious stories
10                    in the mystery we call history
                  (a river blurred with tears
              or a running sea
                  whose fish change color
                      when cast upon the beach)
And the feelthy rich
    get filthier or richer or whatever
        because money really doesn't 'trickle down'
        but rises like anything hot
And they keep getting more medals
20    for bad behavior and for agreeing that Yes
        Justice has been done and
            the stock market is open to everyone Long live usura[1]
            and the jury system is the best ever for
                preserving the status quota[2]
And in fact why not have historians who
            leave blanks in their writings
                to be filled in variously
                    depending on who's in power
                      and the computer makes changes easy
30  And anyway history isn't really history
until it's rewritten
or at least until
it repeats itself
And a lot of genocides and massacres

[1] **usura:** from the word *usury*, to rhyme with quota
[2] **status quota:** a play on the words *status quo* and *quota*

**1. Response**

**a.** Complete the following analysis for any of the poems in this section:

- Who or what do you think is being ridiculed?
- In your opinion, is the ridicule justified? Is the issue important? Explain.
- What is the tone of the attack?
- How is humour or ridicule created in the poem?
- Do you think the poem is an effective satire? Why?

**b.** Many song lyrics are satirical poems set to music. Find a song lyric that you consider to be satirical. Using the questions in part (a) above, complete an analysis of the lyrics. Present your analysis to the class after letting them hear the song.

**2. Literature Studies** *Allegory* To appreciate an **allegory**, it is necessary to go beyond the literal level of the work and come to terms with the deeper symbolic level. Read "St. George" carefully, then speculate on what each character or element on the literal level might symbolize. What belief, attitude, and/or behaviour do you think the poet wishes to change for the better? Compare your analysis with that of a classmate. Did you reach the same conclusions?

An **allegory** is a story with an underlying meaning parallel to but different from the surface meaning. An allegory presents ideas in a concrete, vivid way.

**3. Writing** *Satirical Poem* Write your own satirical poem directed at a human folly or foible that concerns or annoys you. Use any poem in this section as a model if you wish.

**4. Oral Language** *Discussion* As a group, choose one of the poems in this section and discuss its message. Half of your group can support the poet's point of view, while the rest of the group presents opposing points.

Poetry is .../a sort of answer I feel compelled
to give/to my own life.

—*Furugh Farrukhzad*

# Didactic Poetry

Some poets strive to produce positive changes, but prefer to avoid the satirical approach. Instead, their poetry offers explicit advice or moral lessons, and is known as *didactic verse*.

As readers, we rarely wish to be patronized or preached at by poets. For these reasons, didactic poetry works best when it has elements of craft and subtlety.

To what extent would you consider these to be good poems? Subtle poems? Which do you think is the most effective in influencing the reader's thoughts and feelings? Explain.

### Heart
By Suniti Namjoshi

And then there was the woman who had no head,
all heart she was. She was even called Heart, and not
(as one might have expected) the Headless Woman.
Her function in life was to serve other people and this
she did with a willing heart. She cooked, she cleaned,
she baked, she scoured and she was always kind and
loving and gentle, and never once complained of feeling
tired. In the course of time her children grew up,
her husband grew old, eventually he died and then he
was buried. The Headless Woman was all alone. So
she went to the Government to ask for a pension. And
she didn't get it. Now I'm not suggesting that the
Government was brutal. The problem was that she
had no head and couldn't ask.

### The Sunlight
By Chief Dan George

The sunlight does not leave its marks
                    on the grass.
So we, too, pass silently.

# Universal Soldier

By Buffy Sainte-Marie

He's five foot two and he's six feet four
He fights with missiles and with spears
He's all of thirty-one and he's only seventeen
He's been a soldier for a thousand years.

He's a Catholic a Hindu an Atheist a Jain
A Buddhist and a Baptist and a Jew
And he knows he shouldn't kill and he knows he always will
Kill you for me my friend and me for you.

And he's fighting for Canada and he's fighting for France
10   He's fighting for the USA
And he's fighting for the Russians and he's fighting for Japan
And he thinks we'll put an end to war this way.

And he's fighting for democracy, he's fighting for the reds
He says it's for the peace of all
He's the one who must decide who's to live and who's to die
And he never sees the writing on the wall.

But without him how would Hitler have condemned them at Dachau
Without him Caesar would've stood alone
He's the one who gives his body as a weapon of the war
20   And without him all this can't go on.

He's the Universal Soldier and he really is to blame
His orders come from far away no more
They come from him and you and me
And brothers can't you see
This is not the way we put an end to war.

# There Will Come Soft Rains

By Sara Teasdale

There will come soft rains and the smell of the ground,
And swallows circling with their shimmering sound;
And frogs in the pools singing at night,
And wild plum trees in tremulous white;
Robins will wear their feathery fire,
Whistling their whims on a low fence-wire;
And not one will know of the war, not one
Will care at last when it is done.
Not one would mind, neither bird nor tree,
10   If mankind perished utterly;
And Spring herself, when she woke at dawn
Would scarcely know that we were gone.

# I Believe

By Robert Fulghum

I believe that imagination is stronger than knowledge—
That myth is more potent than history.
I believe that dreams are more powerful than facts—
That hope always triumphs over experience—
That laughter is the only cure for grief.
And I believe that love is stronger than death.

I have nothing to say, I am saying it,
and that is poetry.

—*John Cage*

# the laughing heart

By Charles Bukowski

your life is your life.
don't let it be clubbed into dank
submission.
be on the watch.
there are ways out.
there is light somewhere.
it may not be much light but
it beats the
darkness.
10   be on the watch.
the gods will offer you
chances.
know them, take them.
you can't beat death but
you can beat death
in life,
sometimes.
and the more often you
learn to do it,
20   the more light there will
be.
your life is your life.
know it while you have
it.
you are marvelous
the gods wait to delight
in
you.

# The Sun Witness

By Nurunnessa Choudhury

*Translated from the Bengali by the author and Paul Joseph Thompson*

Long ago a young girl
wearing a saffron coloured saree
walked gracefully
on her way—
She moved the square stone
from the white
near-dead grass.
By the lightning speed
of her black hand.

10    Silently, with her gaze,
she commanded the sun
to send its light
down upon everything,
even the white grass.

The sun accepted
her easy command
and came down with humility.

Days after,
she passed beggars in the street,
20    and tucked in her silk saree
to avoid their stains.

Seeing this,
The sun hid behind clouds,
and rain came,
unexpectedly, like tears.

# Take Something Like a Star

## By Robert Frost

O Star (the fairest one in sight),
We grant your loftiness the right
To some obscurity of cloud—
It will not do to say of night,
Since dark is what brings out your light.
Some mystery becomes the proud.
But to be wholly taciturn
In your reserve is not allowed.
Say something to us we can learn
10 By heart and when alone repeat.
Say something! And it says, "I burn."
But say with what degree of heat.
Talk Fahrenheit, talk Centigrade.
Use language we can comprehend.
Tell us what elements you blend.
It gives us strangely little aid,
But does tell something in the end.
And steadfast as Keats' Eremite,
Not even stooping from its sphere
20 It asks a little of us here.
It asks of us a certain height,
So when at times the mob is swayed
To carry praise or blame too far,
We may take something like a star
To stay our minds on and be staid.

**Keats:** John Keats, English poet (1795–1821)

**Eremite:** literally *hermit*, from a line by John Keats: "Like nature's patient, sleepless Eremite."

# non-resident identity

By Mo Khan

*east is east and west is west/ and never the twain shall meet//* i'm running out of patience/ sense my situation/ tense, my ancient body burns/ i learn to bend and turn in self-defence/ self preservation/ cultural invasion/ ethnic mastication/ race-and-nation separation/ face it; nothing sates this age of information// second-generation asian rage/ engaged in recitation/ put my fate into rotation/ mired in contemplation/ tired of waiting for my compensation/ recompense/ i recommence/ i recommend you reconsider your attempts at reconciliation/ rehabilitation/ from your station you can catch the scent of rising

10   incense/ thick, but not disguising my societal demise/ my culture's immolation/ it's immense, but then, are you surprised?// NRI[1]/ pardesi[2]/ made to see my race the way they see it/ day-to-day their prostrate grace/ is what i'm faced with/ hate is hastily replaced/ displaced by warm embraces/ great/ but what's it laced with?/ wait until i'm wasted/ seal my fate// exoticize/ eroticize me/ cauterize my conscious highs/ you're carbon-copying me down to size// my star is rising from the east/ my native tongue is unleashed/ scarred/ but each and every part of my speech/ hearkens to the drone of the sitar/ aur kitna beqaraar hai mera intezaar[3]/ it's hard// i'm yearning/ like a cut sardar[4]

20   returning to his turban/ disregard this urban darkness/ i'm unhesitant to learn/ and unconcerned with/ near and far/ it's evident/ that home/ is more than where you are/ a global resident/ remembering the past but living in the present// embers of your pleasant trust/ combust and turn to conscious dust/ we must adjust/ there is/ no justice./ just us.//

[1]**NRI: non-resident Indian:** common term for South Asian immigrants

[2]**pardesi:** Hindi word meaning "stranger," especially to the country, that is, emigrant

[3]**"aur kitna . . .": Urdu:** "and how chaotic is my wait"

[4]**cut sardar:** a Sikh who shaves and chooses not to wear the turban

**1. Response**
   **a.** For each poem in this section, write a brief summary (one or two sentences) of the moral lesson you think it presents. How explicit is the lesson in each poem? Does the explicitness of the lesson influence your appreciation of the poem? Explain.
   **b.** Which poem says something you strongly agree with? In a short composition, describe how society might change if many people truly took that lesson to heart.
   **c.** Poets who use the free verse form often use line breaks to emphasize certain words and ideas. Look at the line breaks in "the laughing heart" and "The Sun Witness." Identify one line break that effectively emphasizes something that is central to the poem's meaning, explaining how you came to that conclusion. Which poet do you think makes the most effective use of line breaks? Explain.

**2. Language Focus** *Gender*  Study the pronouns used in "The Universal Soldier" and "There Will Come Soft Rains." What underlying assumptions do these pronouns suggest? Do you agree with those assumptions? Give reasons for your point of view.

**3. Literature Studies** *Interpretation*  In a group, choose the one poem in this section that you feel is the most challenging to grasp. Work together to try to enhance your understanding. Pose questions about specific words and phrases and speculate on possible answers. Your goal is to present an interpretation of the poem to the rest of the class.

**4. Media** *Inspirational Poster*  Choose a brief quotation from any of the poems in this section and create an inspirational poster to represent that quotation. You will need to find or create a visual that complements the message in the words. Display your poster in the classroom or around the school.

I would define the poetic effect as the capacity that a text displays for continuing to generate different readings, without ever being completely consumed.

—*Umberto Eco*

# Descriptive Poetry

Descriptive poetry is notable for its vividness. Through memorable descriptions that appeal directly to our senses, descriptive poetry engages our minds, our hearts, and our imaginations.

For each of these poems, identify the specific senses that are being appealed to. Which poem do you think is most effective in painting a mental picture?

*Waves*
Anonymous (from the Arabic)

Waves
bow
before
the shore

courtiers
to their king

and then
withdraw.

*Evening*
By Claire Harris

the lift hums and stops
footsteps dim in the muffled corridor
a key struggles in the lock

the bright scent of onions opens and shuts

*The Eagle*
By Alfred, Lord Tennyson

He clasps the crag with crooked hands;
Close to the sun in lonely lands,
Ringed with the azure world he stands;
The wrinkled sea beneath him crawls;
He watches from the mountain walls,
And like a thunderbolt he falls.

# *Hockey*

By Scott Blaine

The ice is smooth, smooth, smooth.
The air bites to the center
Of warmth and flesh, and I whirl.
It begins in a game ...
The puck swims, skims, veers,
Goes leading my vision
Beyond the chasing reach of my stick.

The air is sharp, steel-sharp.
I suck needles of breathing,
10    And feel the players converge.
It grows to a science ...
We clot, break, drive,
Electrons in motion
In the magnetic pull of the puck.

The play is fast, fierce, tense.
Sticks click and snap like teeth
Of wolves on the scent of a prey.
It ends in the kill ...
I am one of the pack in a mad,
20    Taut leap of desperation
In the wild, slashing drive for the goal.

A poem is like a wine glass in
which you can hold up a little
bit of reality and taste it.
—*Gwen Harwood*

# The Rain Hammers

By Michael Wade

The rain hammers at my window
      with fists abandoned by the wind
      my curtains billow with delight
      at the curious black waters bludgeoning

inside
      a semi-precious bumblebee
      mysteriously hums above
      a plastic flower

eternity becomes
10      the sound of the sea in the night
      the pound of the tide in the black
      the flood of the shore in the dark
      the cry of the gull in the dawn

the sun comes out of the sea
      covered with weed
      surrounded with sound
      cornered by clouds
      and breathes on the world.

# Twilight Entered My Room

By Pandelis Prevelakis

Twilight entered my room
like a red lion.
Its reflected light fell in the mirror
and I felt its soft paws
touching my naked feet.
I stooped under the table
which the day's work had blessed
and saw the sun kissing my feet
with its red tongue.

*Big Ben, Parliament & River Thames—London, England* by Harald Sund

How do you think the effects in this photo were achieved? What effect does the photo have on the viewer? Write a descriptive poem about this image.

# Prelude #1

By T. S. Eliot

The winter evening settles down
With smells of steaks in passageways.
Six o'clock.
The burnt-out ends of smoky days.
And now a gusty shower wraps
The grimy scraps
Of withered leaves about your feet
And newspapers from vacant lots;
The showers beat
On broken blinds and chimney-pots,
And at the corner of the street
A lonely cab-horse steams and stamps.
And then the lighting of the lamps.

# The Spider Holds a Silver Ball

By Emily Dickinson

The Spider holds a Silver Ball
In unperceived Hands—
And dancing softly to Himself
His Yarn of Pearl—unwinds—

He plies from Nought to Nought—
In unsubstantial Trade—
Supplants our Tapestries with His—
In half the period—

An Hour to rear supreme
His Continents of Light—
Then dangle from the Housewife's Broom—
His Boundaries—forgot—

**1. *Response***

**a.** Descriptive poetry often seeks to suggest a particular mood. What is the dominant mood of each poem in this section? Identify specific words or phrases that are instrumental in creating that mood.

**b.** Look closely at the poem "Hockey." What patterns can you detect that help to build a structure for the poem? Do you prefer to write highly structured or less structured poems? Explain.

**c.** Description can capture the experience of hearing, seeing, smelling, tasting, and touching. Based on your reading of the poems in this section, including those on page 207, which of the five kinds of sensory experiences are most often described? Why? Write your own descriptive poem, focussing on one or more of the five senses.

**2. *Language Conventions*** *Vivid Language* There are several keys to good description: forceful verbs, specific nouns, colourful adjectives, lively adverbs. Create a four-column chart with those four headings. Drawing from all the poems in this section, find examples to complete your chart. Add some of your own examples to each column.

**3. *Media*** *Multimedia Presentation* Create a multimedia presentation based on one or more of the poems in this section. Your presentation may incorporate computers, video or audio tape, CDs, magazine illustrations, original artwork, oral commentary, live music, movement, or dance, in any combination. The entire poem must be included somehow in your work.

As honey sweetens/the mouth
readily/a poem should
make sense/right away.

*—Atakuri Molla*

# Narrative Poetry

Narrative poetry tells a story. It is concerned with characters, contexts (time, place, and situation), and conflict. Often the poet maintains a tight focus on the thoughts and feelings of the protagonist, and the details of the story are only suggested. This obliges the reader to participate in the creative process to fill in the gaps.

As you read the poems below, use your imagination to see beyond the few details the poets provide. What stories suggest themselves to you?

## My Hands
By Takeo Nakano

My hands tremble
As I sign my naturalization
    papers
Making me a Canadian
    citizen
And Canada my final resting
    place.

## Day After Day . . .
By Wang Hung Kung
*Translated by Kenneth Rexroth*

Day after day the rain falls.
Week after week the grass grows.
Year after year the river flows.
Seventy years, seventy years,
The wheel of dreams revolves.

## Meeting at Night
By Robert Browning

The gray sea and the long black land;
And the yellow half-moon large and low;
And the startled little waves that leap
In fiery ringlets from their sleep,
As I gain the cove with pushing prow,
And quench its speed i' the slushy sand.

Then a mile of warm sea-scented beach;
Three fields to cross till a farm appears;
A tap at the pane, the quick sharp scratch
And blue spurt of a lighted match,
And a voice less loud, through its joys and fears,
Than the two hearts beating each to each!

# Gaining Yardage

By Leo Dangel

The word *friend* never came up
between Arlo and me—we're farm neighbors
who hang around together, walk beans,
pick rocks, and sit on the bench
at football games, weighing the assets
of the other side's cheerleaders.
Tonight we lead 48 to 6, so the coach
figures sending us both in is safe.
I intercept an underthrown pass
10   only because I'm playing the wrong position,
and Arlo is right there to block for me
because he's in the wrong place,
so we gallop up the field, in the clear
until their second-string quarterback
meets us at the five-yard line,
determined to make up for his bad throw.
Arlo misses the block, the guy has me
by the leg and jersey, and going down,
I flip the ball back to Arlo, getting up,
20   who fumbles, and their quarterback
almost recovers, then bobbles the ball
across the goal line, and our coach,
who told even the guys with good hands
never to mess around with laterals,
must feel his head exploding,
when Arlo and I dive on the ball together
in the end zone and dance and slap
each other on the back.
They give Arlo the touchdown, which rightly
30   should be mine, but I don't mind,
and I suppose we are friends, and will be,
unless my old man or his decides to move
to another part of the country.

# *Snake*

By D. H. Lawrence

A snake came to my water-trough
On a hot, hot day, and I in pyjamas for the heat,
To drink there.

In the deep, strange-scented shade of the great dark carob-tree
I came down the steps with my pitcher
And must wait, must stand and wait, for there he was at the trough
    before me.

He reached down from a fissure in the earth-wall in the gloom
And trailed his yellow-brown slackness soft-bellied down, over the
10     edge of the stone trough
And rested his throat upon the stone bottom,
And where the water had dripped from the tap, in a small clearness,
He sipped with his straight mouth,
Softly drank through his straight gums, into his slack long body,
Silently.

Someone was before me at my water-trough,
And I, like a second comer, waiting.

He lifted his head from his drinking, as cattle do,
And looked at me vaguely, as drinking cattle do,
20 And flickered his two-forked tongue from his lips, and mused a
    moment,
And stooped and drank a little more,
Being earth-bronze, earth-golden from the burning bowels of the
    earth
On the day of Sicilian July, with Etna[1] smoking.

The voice of my education said to me
He must be killed,
For in Sicily the black, black snakes are innocent, the gold are
    venomous.

---

[1]**Etna:** Situated in Sicily, Italy, Mount Etna is the highest active volcano in Europe.

30    And voices in me said, If you were a man
You would take a stick and break him now, and finish him off.

But must I confess how I liked him,
How glad I was he had come like a guest in quiet, to drink at my
    water-trough
And depart peaceful, pacified, and thankless,
Into the burning bowels of this earth?

Was it cowardice, that I dared not kill him?
Was it perversity, that I longed to talk to him?
Was it humility, to feel so honoured?
40    I felt so honoured.

And yet those voices:
*If you were not afraid, you would kill him!*

And truly I was afraid, I was most afraid,
But even so, honoured still more
That he should seek my hospitality
From out the dark door of the secret earth.

He drank enough
And lifted his head, dreamily, as one who has drunken,
And flickered his tongue like a forked night on the air, so black,
50    Seeming to lick his lips,
And looked around like a god, unseeing, into the air,
And slowly turned his head,
And slowly, very slowly, as if thrice adream,
Proceeded to draw his slow length curving round
And climb again the broken bank of my wall-face.

And as he put his head into that dreadful hole,
And as he slowly drew up, snake-easing his shoulders, and entered
    farther,
A sort of horror, a sort of protest against his withdrawing into that
60    horrid black hole,
Deliberately going into the blackness, and slowly drawing himself
    after,
Overcame me now his back was turned.

I looked around, I put down my pitcher,
I picked up a clumsy log
And threw it at the water-trough with a clatter.

I think it did not hit him,
But suddenly that part of him that was left behind convulsed in
    undignified haste,
70    Writhed like lightning, and was gone
Into the black hole, the earth-lipped fissure in the wall-front,
At which, in the intense still noon, I stared with fascination.

And immediately I regretted it.
I thought how paltry, how vulgar, what a mean act!
I despised myself and the voices of my accursed human education.

And I thought of the albatross,
And I wished he would come back, my snake.

For he seemed to me again like a king,
Like a king in exile, uncrowned in the underworld,
80    Now due to be crowned again.

And so, I missed my chance with one of the lords
Of life.
And I have something to expiate;
A pettiness.

*Carolyn Walking, N.M.* by Marilyn Conway

Use one of the poems in this section as a model and write a narrative poem that tells a story inspired by this photo. You could use first person, third person, objective, or omniscient point of view.

# Legend

By Judith Wright

The blacksmith's boy went out with a rifle
and a black dog running behind.
Cobwebs snatched at his feet,
rivers hindered him,
thorn-branches caught at his eyes to make him blind
and the sky turned into an unlucky opal,
but he didn't mind.
I can break branches, I can swim rivers, I can stare out
    any spider I meet,
10    said he to his dog and his rifle.

The blacksmith's boy went over the paddocks
with his old black hat on his head.
Mountains jumped in his way,
rocks rolled down on him,
and the old crow cried, You'll soon be dead;
and the rain came down like mattocks.
But he only said
I can climb mountains, I can dodge rocks, I can shoot
    an old crow any day.
20    And he went on over the paddocks.

When he came to the end of the day the sun began falling.
Up came the night ready to swallow him,
like the barrel of a gun,
like an old black hat,
like a black dog hungry to follow him.
Then the pigeon, the magpie and the dove began wailing,
and the grass lay down to pillow him.
His rifle broke, his hat blew away and his dog was gone,
and the sun was falling.

30    But in front of the night the rainbow stood on a mountain
just as his heart foretold.
He ran like a hare,
he climbed like a fox,
he caught it in his hands, the colours and the cold—

like a bar of ice, like the columns of a fountain,
like a ring of gold.
The pigeon, the magpie and the dove flew up to stare,
and the grass stood up again on the mountain.

The blacksmith's boy hung the rainbow on his shoulder,
40    instead of his broken gun.
Lizards ran out to see,
snakes made way for him,
and the rainbow shone as brightly as the sun.
All the world said, Nobody is braver, nobody is bolder,
nobody else has done
anything to equal it. He went home as easy as could be
with the swinging rainbow on his shoulder.

# The Child Who Walks Backwards

By Lorna Crozier

My next-door neighbour tells me
her child runs into things.
Cupboard corners and doorknobs
have pounded their shapes
into his face. She says
he is bothered by dreams,
rises in sleep from his bed
to steal through the halls
and plummet like a wounded bird
10    down the flight of stairs.

This child who climbed my maple
with the sureness of a cat,
trips in his room, cracks
his skull on the bedpost,
smacks his cheeks on the floor.
When I ask about the burns

on the back of his knee,
his mother tells me
he walks backwards
into fireplace grates
20  or sits and stares at flames
while sparks burn stars in his skin.

Other children write their names
on the casts that hold
his small bones.
His mother tells me
he runs into things,
walks backwards,
breaks his leg
30  while she lies
sleeping

## *Subway Exit: Spring*

By Jane Poston

                                        a green world of pigeons.
                                into
                              ator
                            cal-
                          es-
                        way
                      sub-
                    St.
                  ton
                ing-
              Arl-
            the
          via
        born
      re-
    I am
  ing
Each morn-

**1. Response**

**a.** For any two poems in this section, complete the following analysis:

- What is your best estimate of when and where the narrative takes place?
- What are the characteristics of the narrator or protagonist?
- What conflict, if any, does the narrative describe?
- What do you think is the main purpose of the poem?

**b.** Discuss the advantages and disadvantages of telling a story through verse rather than prose. Come to a consensus on at least three advantages and three disadvantages. Provide support for your positions, using specific references to the poems in this section, where possible.

**c.** In your opinion, which poem in this unit tells the most powerful and/or engaging story? Explore your response in a brief piece of writing, supplying the reasons for your preference. How does your opinion compare with the responses of your classmates?

**2. _Oral Language_** _Poetry Performance_  In groups, prepare a dramatic performance of either Judith Wright's "Legend" or D. H. Lawrence's "Snake." What special techniques can your group use to enhance the impact of your performance? After your presentation, reflect in writing on which techniques were most successful. Include suggestions that will help you prepare future oral presentations.

**3. _Media_** _Storyboard_  Assume you were going to create a video to represent one of the poems in this section. In preparation for the filming, create a storyboard outlining the various shots your video camera would record. Your storyboard should contain at least ten frames. Accompany each frame with one or two sentences that specify details such as the camera angle, lighting requirements, and positioning of characters and so on.

> Listen, real poetry doesn't say anything,
> it just ticks off the possibilities.
> Opens all doors.
> You can walk through any one that suits you.
> —_Jim Morrison_

# Reflective Poetry

Poems that search for deep truths and pose the essential questions of existence are classified as *reflective poetry*. Here the poets contemplate life and what it means to be human. They invite us to reflect on matters of identity and purpose: Who am I? Why am I here? Is there an ultimate purpose to life? What is the nature of happiness?

Once you have read the following two poems, write down the essential questions that the poems imply. Are any answers suggested in these lines? Explain. How would you answer the questions?

from *Auguries of Innocence*
By William Blake

To see a World in a Grain of Sand,
And a Heaven in a Wild Flower,
Hold Infinity in the palm of your hand,
And Eternity in an hour.

from *I Have Had to Learn to Live With My Face*
By Diane Wakoski

I look at pictures of myself as a child.
I looked lumpy, unformed, like a piece of dough,
and it has been my task as a human being
to carve out a mind, carve out a face,
carve out a shape with arms & legs, to put a voice inside,
and to make a person from a presence.
And I don't think I'm unique.
I think a thousand of you, at least, can look at those old photos,
reflect on your life
and see your own sculpture at work.

# This Morning I Sat

By Rosalie Fowler

This morning I sat
indolent and limp
against a window pane
and watched a frantic sparrow
defying my lean cat.

The cat was taut
with leap and speed
and stealth and strength.
The bird had only poetry to wield
10   and lost.

Cats eat up grace with relish.
But they are poets too
and can create cunning
and flights of terror
with their eyes.

A small shudder
rippled down my flesh.

Do I have wings or claws?

Poetry ... is another way to
be hurled straight into
the heart of God.
—*Marjorie Holmes*

# The Real Math

By Oscar Peñaranda

Here's a clue
if you take what I did
and to that add my dreams
divide by what I didn't do
and said I would do
multiply that by what I didn't say
yet did just the same
then subtract what I could have done
but said to myself impossible

10    Then you have something
on me
yet after all this
you can find it in your heart

to erase everything
take nothing before and beyond
erase all
and gather the answer of who I am
cradled in your hands
only at that moment

20    then you can begin
to call me by a
name

if not
let me slide and remain

—anonymous

# Nothing Is Like Nothing Else

By Elizabeth Brewster

When I was young and knew no better
I was always wanting to compare this to that:
Hearts might be cold as ice cream cones:
Water shone like flashlights;
Autumn leaves were mustard
On the sky's blue china plate.

But now I know different.
Now I know that nothing is like nothing else.
A white plate is a white plate, smooth, glossy;
10 Snow is another whiteness: not powdery,
Not like wool or silk or feathers,
But like itself, cold, dense, soft,
And yet sometimes hard, sometimes pointed,
Reflecting the sky, which is not like blue nylon,
But has its own special colour, texture, absence of texture.
And there are so many objects,
So many whites, blues, transparencies,
That the eye and the mind must be careful,
Must work very hard not to be confused by them.

20 And when I get beyond objects
(Seashells, mirrors, bottles of ginger ale,
Daisy petals, and all the rest)
And try to consider minds and motives
And poetry and politics
And work and friendship—
Then language is difficult indeed,
Since minds are never alike
And never like snow.

# *The New House*

By Maya Angelou

What words
have smashed against
these walls,
crashed up and down these
halls,
lain mute and then drained
their meanings out and into
these floors?

What feelings, long since
10    dead,
streamed vague yearnings
below this ceiling
light?
In some dimension,
which I cannot know,
the shadows of
another still exist. I bring my
memories, held too long in check,
to let them here shoulder
20    space and place to be.

And when I leave to
find another house,
I wonder, what among
these shades will be
left of me.

# *Death of a Young Son by Drowning*

By Margaret Atwood

He, who navigated with success
the dangerous river of his own birth
once more set forth

on a voyage of discovery
into the land I floated on
but could not touch to claim.

His feet slid on the bank,
the currents took him;
he swirled with ice and trees in the swollen water

10    and plunged into distant regions,
his head a bathysphere;
through his eyes' thin glass bubbles

he looked out, reckless adventurer
on a landscape stranger than Uranus
we have all been to and some remember.

There was an accident; the air locked,
he was hung in the river like a heart.
They retrieved the swamped body,

cairn of my plans and future charts,
20    with poles and hooks
from among the nudging logs.

It was spring, the sun kept shining, the new grass
lept to solidity;
my hands glistened with details.

After the long trip I was tired of waves.
My foot hit rock. The dreamed sails
collapsed, ragged.

    I planted him in this country
    like a flag.

# My Father Is a Simple Man

By Luis Omar Salinas

I walk to town with my father
to buy a newspaper. He walks slower
than I do so I must slow up.
The street is filled with children.
We argue about the price
of pomegranates, I convince
him it is the fruit of scholars.
He has taken me on this journey
and it's been lifelong.
10   He's sure I'll be healthy
so long as I eat more oranges,
and tells me the orange
has seeds and so is perpetual;
and we too will come back
like the orange trees.
I ask him what he thinks
about death and he says
he will gladly face it when
it comes but won't jump
20   out in front of a car.
I'd gladly give my life
for this man with a sixth
grade education, whose kindness
and patience are true ...
The truth of it is, he's the scholar,
and when the bitter-hard reality
comes at me like a punishing
evil stranger, I can always
remember that here was a man
30   who was a worker and provider,
who learned the simple facts
in life and lived by them,
who held no pretense.
And when he leaves without
benefit of fanfare or applause
I shall have learned what little
there is about greatness.

# *Ethics*

## By Linda Pastan

In ethics class so many years ago
our teacher asked this question every fall:
if there were a fire in a museum
which would you save, a Rembrandt painting
or an old woman who hadn't many
years left anyhow? Restless on hard chairs
caring little for pictures or old age
we'd opt one year for life, the next for art
and always half-heartedly. Sometimes

10  the woman borrowed my grandmother's face
leaving her usual kitchen to wander
some drafty, half-imagined museum.
One year, feeling clever, I replied
why not let the woman decide herself?
Linda, the teacher would report, eschews
the burdens of responsibility.
This fall in a real museum I stand
before a real Rembrandt, old woman,
or nearly so, myself. The colors

20  within this frame are darker than autumn,
darker even than winter—the browns of earth,
though earth's most radiant elements burn
through the canvas. I know now that woman
and painting and season are almost one
and all beyond saving by children.

**Rembrandt:** Rembrandt Harmenszoon van Rijn (1606–1669), a Dutch painter.

Poetry is the opening and closing of a door,
leaving those who look through to guess
about what is seen during a moment.
—*Carl Sandburg*

*Philosophy and Meditation* by Rembrandt. 1632. Oil on wood. Musée du Louvre, Paris

Consider this painting and the teacher's question in "Ethics." How would you respond to that question?

**1. *Response***

**a.** "This Morning I Sat" and "The New Math" both explore the issue of identity, asking the question, "Who and what am I?" Which poem do you prefer? Why?

**b.** The speaker in Linda Pastan's "Ethics" concludes by suggesting an answer to the ethical question posed at the beginning of the poem. Express the answer in your own words. Do you agree with that answer? Explain.

**c.** Which of the poems in this section ends on a note of uncertainty? Why do you think uncertainty might be a quality of many reflective poems?

**d.** Choose one poem in this section and compose your own poetic answer to the question it poses.

**2. *Critical Thinking*** Reflective poetry deals with essential questions about people and about life. In a group, brainstorm a list of essential questions that could become the starting point for a reflective poem. Your list should contain ten questions. Compare lists in a class discussion. Generally speaking, can the questions you framed be answered definitively? What does this suggest about the process of seeking answers to such questions?

**3. *Language Conventions*** *Rhetorical Questions* To create a reflective poem, a poet could use **rhetorical questions**, as Maya Angelou does in "The New House." Reread her poem to see how she has used rhetorical questions. How many of the essential questions you developed in activity 2 were rhetorical? Use one of them as a starting point for a new poem.

**Rhetorical questions** are questions asked for effect, rather than in a search for information.

**4. *Writing*** *Celebratory Poem* In "My Father Is a Simple Man," the narrator describes and celebrates the essence of a father. Using the poem as a model, write your own poem in which you reflect on the life of a loved one and celebrate what that person means to you. As Salinas does, include specific details that bring the person to life.

# The Test of Time

Some poems defy time. Instead of fading as the years pass, they flourish and grow richer. We read them and reread them, study them and appreciate them. All the following poems have transcended the moment at which they were written and have been woven into the fabric of our culture.

There are some important questions to consider as you read these poems. What qualities make a poem a *classic?* Who decides which poems do and do not receive this honour? What are the benefits and the dangers of valuing some works far more than others?

"A good poem is a contribution to reality.

The world is never the same once a good poem has been added to it. A good poem helps to change the shape and significance of the universe, helps to extend [people]'s knowledge of [themselves] and the world around [them]."
     —Dylan Thomas

"Poetry fosters a passionate interest in language, its rhythm and emotional power. It inspires a willingness to write and revise until a poem is the closest you can get to what you want to say."
     —Barbara Sapergia

"In Inuit, the word to make poetry is the word to breathe; both are derivatives of *anerca*, the soul, that which is eternal: the breath of life."
     —Edmund Carpenter

"A poem is a watch designed
To tick forever in the mind."
     —Fred Cogswell

"Since flesh can't stay,
we pass the words along."
     —Erica Jong

# La Belle Dame Sans Merci

By John Keats

O what can ail thee, knight-at-arms,
    Alone and palely loitering?
The sedge has withered from the lake,
    And no birds sing.

O what can ail thee, knight-at-arms,
    So haggard and so woe-begone?
The squirrel's granary is full,
    And the harvest's done.

I see a lily on thy brow,
10          With anguish moist and fever dew,
And on thy cheeks a fading rose
    Fast withereth too.

I met a lady in the meads,
    Full beautiful—a faery's child,
Her hair was long, her foot was light,
    And her eyes were wild.

I made a garland for her head,
    And bracelets too, and fragrant zone;
She looked at me as she did love,
20          And made sweet moan.

I set her on my pacing steed,
    And nothing else saw all day long,
For sidelong would she bend, and sing
    A faery's song.

She found me roots of relish sweet,
    And honey wild, and manna dew,
And sure in language strange she said,
    "I love thee true."

---

**La Belle Dame Sans Merci:** the beautiful woman without mercy

She took me to her elfin grot,
30     And there she wept, and sighed full sore,
And there I shut her wild wild eyes
    With kisses four.

And there she lulléd me asleep,
    And there I dreamed—Ah! woe betide!
The latest dream I ever dreamed
    On the cold hill side.

I saw pale kings and princes too,
    Pale warriors, death-pale were they all;
They cried—"La Belle Dame sans Merci
40     Hath thee in thrall!"

I saw their starved lips in the gloam,
    With horrid warning gapéd wide,
And I awoke and found me here,
    On the cold hill's side.

And this is why I sojourn here,
    Alone and palely loitering,
Though the sedge has withered from the lake,
    And no birds sing.

# Ulysses

By Alfred, Lord Tennyson

    It little profits that an idle king,
By this still hearth, among these barren crags,
Matched with an agéd wife, I mete and dole
Unequal laws unto a savage race,
That hoard, and sleep, and feed, and know not me.

    I cannot rest from travel; I will drink
Life to the lees. All times I have enjoyed
Greatly, have suffered greatly, both with those
That loved me, and alone; on shore, and when

10 Through scudding drifts the rainy Hyades
Vexed the dim sea. I am become a name;
For always roaming with a hungry heart
Much have I seen and known—cities of men
And manners, climates, councils, governments,
Myself not least, but honored of them all—
And drunk delight of battle with my peers,
Far on the ringing plains of windy Troy.
I am a part of all that I have met;
Yet all experience is an arch wherethrough
20 Gleams that untraveled world, whose margin fades
For ever and for ever when I move.
How dull it is to pause, to make an end,
To rust unburnished, not to shine in use!
As though to breathe were life. Life piled on life
Were all too little, and of one to me
Little remains; but every hour is saved
From that eternal silence, something more,
A bringer of new things; and vile it were
For some three suns to store and hoard myself,
30 And this gray spirit yearning in desire
To follow knowledge like a sinking star,
Beyond the utmost bound of human thought.

    This is my son, mine own Telemachus,
To whom I leave the scepter and the isle—
Well-loved of me, discerning to fulfill
This labour by slow prudence to make mild
A rugged people, and through soft degrees
Subdue them to the useful and the good.
Most blameless is he, centered in the sphere
40 Of common duties, decent not to fail
In offices of tenderness, and pay
Meet adoration to my household gods,
When I am gone. He works his work, I mine.

    There lies the port; the vessel puffs her sail:
There gloom the dark, broad seas. My mariners,
Souls that have toiled, and wrought, and thought with me—
That ever with a frolic welcome took
The thunder and the sunshine, and opposed

**Hyades:** a group of stars that, in ancient times, was believed to be a messenger of spring rain

**Telemachus:** In Greek mythology, and in Homer's *The Odyssey*, Telemachus was the son of Ulysses and Penelope.

Free hearts, free foreheads—you and I are old;
50  Old age hath yet his honor and his toil.
Death closes all; but something ere the end,
Some work of noble note, may yet be done,
Not unbecoming men that strove with Gods.
The lights begin to twinkle from the rocks;
The long day wanes; the slow moon climbs; the deep
Moans round with many voices. Come, my friends.
'Tis not too late to seek a newer world.
Push off, and sitting well in order smite
The sounding furrows; for my purpose holds
60  To sail beyond the sunset, and the baths
Of all the western stars, until I die.
It may be that the gulfs will wash us down;
It may be we shall touch the Happy Isles,
And see the great Achilles, whom we knew.
Though much is taken, much abides; and though
We are not now that strength which in old days
Moved earth and heaven, that which we are, we are:
One equal temper of heroic hearts,
Made weak by time and fate, but strong in will
70  To strive, to seek, to find, and not to yield.

# *A Bird Came Down*

By Emily Dickinson

A Bird came down the Walk—
He did not know I saw—
He bit an Angleworm in halves
And ate the fellow, raw,

And then he drank a Dew
From a convenient Grass—
And then hopped sidewise to the Wall
To let a Beetle pass—

He glanced with rapid eyes
10  That hurried all around—
They looked like frightened Beads, I thought—
He stirred his Velvet Head

Like one in danger, Cautious,
I offered him a Crumb
And he unrolled his feathers
And rowed him softer home—

Than Oars divide the Ocean,
Too silver for a seam—
Or Butterflies, off Banks of Noon
20  Leap, plashless as they swim.


# The Song My Paddle Sings

By Pauline Johnson

West wind, blow from your prairie nest
Blow from the mountains, blow from the west.
The sail is idle, the sailor too;
O! wind of the west, we wait for you.
Blow, blow!
I have wooed you so,
But never a favour you bestow.
You rock your cradle the hills between,
But scorn to notice my white lateen.

10  I stow the sail, unship the mast:
I wooed you long but my wooing's past;
My paddle will lull you into rest.
O! drowsy wind of the drowsy west,
Sleep, sleep,
By your mountain steep,
Or down where the prairie grasses sweep!
Now fold in slumber your laggard wings,
For soft is the song my paddle sings.

August is laughing across the sky,
20   Laughing while paddle, canoe and I,
Drift, drift,
Where the hills uplift
On either side of the current swift.

The river rolls in its rocky bed;
My paddle is plying its way ahead;
Dip, dip,
While the waters flip
In foam as over their breast we slip.

And oh, the river runs swifter now;
30   The eddies circle about my bow.
Swirl, swirl!
How the ripples curl
In many a dangerous pool awhirl!

And forward far the rapids roar,
Fretting their margin for evermore.
Dash, dash,
With a mighty crash,
They seethe, and boil, and bound, and splash.

Be strong, O paddle! be brave, canoe!
40   The reckless waves you must plunge into.
Reel, reel.
On your trembling keel,
But never a fear my craft will feel.

We've raced the rapid, we're far ahead!
The river slips through its silent bed.
Sway, sway,
As the bubbles spray
And fall in tinkling tunes away.

And up on the hills against the sky,
50   A fir tree rocking its lullaby,
Swings, swings,
Its emerald wings,
Swelling the song that my paddle sings.

# Dulce Et Decorum Est

Bent double, like old beggars under sacks,
Knock-kneed, coughing like hags, we cursed through sludge,
Till on the haunting flares we turned our backs,
And towards our distant rest began to trudge.
Men marched asleep. Many had lost their boots,
But limped on, blood-shod. All went lame, all blind;
Drunk with fatigue; deaf even to the hoots
Of gas-shells dropping softly behind.
Gas! GAS! Quick, boys!—An ecstasy of fumbling,
10    Fitting the clumsy helmets just in time,
But someone still was yelling out and stumbling
And flound'ring like a man in fire or lime.—
Dim through the misty panes and thick green light,
As under a green sea, I saw him drowning.

In all my dreams, before my helpless sight,
He plunges at me, guttering, choking, drowning.

If in some smothering dreams, you too could pace
Behind the wagon that we flung him in,
And watch the white eyes writhing in his face,
20    His hanging face, like a devil's sick of sin,
If you could hear, at every jolt, the blood
Come gargling from the froth-corrupted lungs
Obscene as cancer, bitter as the cud
Of vile, incurable sores on innocent tongues,—
My friend, you would not tell with such high zest
To children ardent for some desperate glory,
The old lie: *Dulce et decorum est*
*Pro patria mori.*[1]

---

[1] ***Dulce et decorum est pro patria mori:*** It is sweet and proper to die for your country. (A Latin quotation from the Roman poet, Horace)

# *Harlem*

By Langston Hughes

What happens to a dream deferred?

> Does it dry up
> like a raisin in the sun?
> Or fester like a sore—
> And then run?
> Does it stink like rotten meat?
> Or crust and sugar over—
> like a syrupy sweet?
>
> Maybe it just sags
> like a heavy load.
>
> *Or does it explode?*

10

If not poetry, then what?
   —*Rosario Castellanos*

With me poetry has not been
a purpose, but a passion.
   —*Edgar Allan Poe*

**1.** *Response*
   **a.** Describe some of the challenges you faced as a reader, as you read the poems in this section.
   **b.** Why do you think people continue to study these and other challenging poems despite the obstacles?

**2.** *Literature Studies* *Interpretation and Appreciation* Interpretation involves understanding a poem's theme and/or message—its literal and symbolic meanings. Appreciation involves enjoying the artistry of a poem—the creative manipulation of language and poetic form. In a sustained piece of writing (at least two pages long), offer your own interpretation and appreciation of one poem in this section. You should explain what you think the poem is about, provide examples of the author's poetic skill, and suggest why you think the poem has stood the test of time.

**3.** *Research and Inquiry* Use your research skills to compile essential background information on one of the poets who is featured in this section. You might give an overview of the poet's career, list his or her major poetic works, summarize characteristic themes, and comment on the poet's reputation and accomplishments. Include any other details or material that you think would help a reader discover the context for the poet's work. Present the background information in an engaging way, incorporating visuals if possible.

**4.** *Making Connections* Using library resources or the Internet, find one additional classic poem that you particularly like. Read the poem aloud to a group or the class, and explain why you selected that particular poem. How is it like or unlike the poems in this section?

# Biographies

Maya Angelou has worked as an actor, teacher, and activist. The first of her autobiographical books, *I Know Why the Caged Bird Sings*, gained universal recognition. She has published many poems, and wrote poetry for Clinton's inauguration, and the UN's 50th birthday.

Margaret Atwood's poetic reputation was established in 1966 when *The Circle Game* won the Governor General's Award. She has published numerous books of poetry, including the well-known collection, *The Journals of Susanna Moodie: Poems*. She is also an award-winning novelist, winning the Governor General's Award in 1985 for *The Handmaid's Tale*, and the Booker Prize in 2000 for her novel, *The Blind Assassin*.

Wystan Hugh Auden was born in 1907. In 1930, his collection, *Poems*, established him as an important and influential poet in England. He also wrote plays and librettos, and was a noted editor and essayist. He died in Vienna in 1973.

Elizabeth Barrett Browning was born in England in 1806. Her first poetry collection, *An Essay on Mind and Other Poems*, was published anonymously. In 1844, her collection, *Poems*, gained the attention of the poet Robert Browning. They eloped in 1846. Barrett's *Sonnets from the Portuguese*, dedicated to her husband, was published in 1850, and her verse novel, *Aurora Leigh*, in 1857. She died in Florence in 1861.

Elizabeth Brewster was born in New Brunswick in 1922. She has won numerous awards for her poetry, including the President's Silver Medal for Poetry in 1979, and the Saskatchewan Arts Boards, Lifetime Award for Excellence in the Arts, in 1995.

Charles Bukowski's poetry was first published in the 1940s, and then he allegedly gave up writing for the next 20 years. However, his poetry did continue to appear in many small literary publications during that time. Although he wasn't associated with the major Beat writers, his informal style and non-conforming literary approach appeal to readers of Beat poetry.

Robert "Robbie" Burns was born in Scotland in 1759. Although poverty limited his formal education, he read widely. His first poetry collection, published in 1786, was an immediate success, and his later literary works—consisting almost entirely of songs—included the well-known New Year's Eve song, "Auld Lang Syne." He died in 1796.

Nurunnessa Choudhury has published a collection called *The Sun Witness*. She also translated the anthology *I See Cleopatra and Other Poems* with Paul Joseph Thompson.

Wendy Cope was born in 1945 in the south of England. Her collection, *Making Cocoa for Kingsley Amis*, contains literary jokes and parodies in the style of some well-known poets.

Lorna Crozier grew up in Swift Current, Saskatchewan. Along with other Saskatchewan writers, she has founded a monthly writing workshop jokingly named *The Moose Jaw Movement*. In 1992, her poetry collection, *Inventing the Hawk*, won the Governor General's Award.

Edward Estlin Cummings became known as an experimental poet, due to his unconventional use of form, punctuation, spelling, and syntax. Although his name often appears without capitalization, this was never at the legal request, or even wish, of Cummings himself. It was one publisher's style decision, which was adopted by subsequent publishers as the "correct" style.

Leo Dangel's collections of poetry include *Home From the Field*, *Hogs and Personals: Poems*, and *Old Man Brunner Country*.

Emily Dickinson was born in Massachusetts in 1830. Although she remained in almost total physical isolation from the outside world most of her life, she maintained many correspondences and read widely. She was an extremely prolific poet, but was not publicly recognized during her lifetime. Her first volume of poetry was published posthumously in 1890, and the last in 1955. She died in 1886.

MARY DI MICHELE was born in Italy in 1949, and immigrated to Canada in 1955. She has worked as poetry editor for *Poetry Toronto*, and for *Toronto Life*. She has won a number of awards for her poetry.

GAIL DUSENBERY'S poems have appeared in *Wild Dog, Cow, Poetry* (Chicago), *Poems Read in the Spirit of Peace and Gladness*, and *Free Poems Among Friends*. Her collection of poems, *The Mark*, was published in 1967.

THOMAS STEARNS ELIOT was born in Missouri in 1888, but settled in England in 1914. His first book of poems—*Prufrock and Other Observations*—immediately established him as a leading poet after its publication in 1917. Eliot remains an important figure in poetry and literary criticism throughout the English-speaking world. He received the Nobel Prize for Literature in 1948, and died in London in 1965.

LAWRENCE FERLINGHETTI was born in Yonkers, New York in 1919. He is recognized as one of the most important and influential poets of the "Beat" movement. By 1952, he had established himself as a writer, artist, and political activist. Along with a friend, he opened the City Lights bookstore in San Francisco, which became a mecca for writers and artists.

ROBERT FROST was born in San Francisco in 1874. His first two poetry collections—*A Boy's Will* and *North of Boston*—established his reputation as a poet. His later poetry collections won him more fame and honours, including four Pulitzer Prizes. He died in Boston in 1963.

MARY E. FRYE. Although the poem "Do Not Stand at My Grave and Weep" is attributed to Mary E. Frye, it was "formerly attributed to Native American sources."

ROBERT FULGHUM'S first published essay, "All I Really Need to Know I Learned in Kindergarten," evolved over seven years into 14 million books in 93 countries, a syndicated newspaper column, and a theatre piece.

NIKKI GIOVANNI is a writer of prose and of adult and children's poetry, and is also well-known for her poetry recitals. She has received many awards for her written and performed poetry.

LANGSTON HUGHES was born in Missouri in 1902. He wrote novels, short stories, poetry, and plays, and his work was influenced greatly by jazz. He was part of the Harlem Renaissance of the 1920s. He died in 1967.

GARY HYLAND lectures at the University of Regina, and is an award-winning poet and editor. His books include *Just off Main*, *Street of Dreams*, and *After Atlantis*.

PAULINE JOHNSON was one of Canada's most popular and successful entertainers in the early 1900s, giving hundreds of recitals of her poetry countrywide. She was the first Aboriginal poet to have had her work published in Canada.

JOHN KEATS was an English Romantic poet, born in London, England, in 1795. Although he studied medicine, he never practised his profession, preferring to write poetry instead. His first volume of poetry, published in 1817, received negative reviews. In 1820, he published his third and best volume of poetry, *Lamia, Isabella, The Eve of St. Agnes and Other Poems*.

PEGGY SMITH KRACHUN grew up in Placentia, the former French capital of Newfoundland. She is a freelance writer, but also sings and writes songs. Krachun co-edited the short story collection *Doors Held Ajar* with Isobel Brown and Nellie P. Strowbridge.

DAVID HERBERT LAWRENCE was a novelist, poet, short story writer, and essayist. His radical views were a continual source of controversy and his novel, *Lady Chatterley's Lover,* involved him in a much-publicized censorship case.

IRVING LAYTON, poet, short story writer, essayist, and professor, was born in Romania in 1912. Since the early 1940s, he has been recognized in Canada as a versatile, revolutionary, and controversial poet of the "modern" school. He was nominated by Italy and Korea for the Nobel Prize in 1981 and received a Canada Council Award in 1967.

BETTY LIES is a poet in the schools for the New Jersey State Council on the Arts, and is working on a book temporarily entitled *Earth's Daughters: Stories of Women in Classical Mythology.*

GWENDOLYN MACEWEN was born in Toronto in 1941. She published her first poem at 17, and won the Governor General's Award at 27. During her writing career, she published 15 volumes of poetry, two novels, and a number of radio plays. MacEwen's work is included in most major Canadian anthologies. She died in 1987.

MATEI MARKWEI was born in Ghana. He is an ordained minister who attended Lincoln University, Pennsylvania, and Yale University. He contributed toward writing the play *The Griot*—which traditionally means a West African storyteller.

OGDEN NASH was born in New York in 1902. He published his first book for children, *The Cricket of Caradon*, in 1925, and his first poem appeared in *The New Yorker* in 1932. Nash published 19 books of poetry throughout his lifetime, and is probably best known for his limericks.

WILFRED OWEN was born in England in 1893. He taught English in France from 1913 to 1915. Then, in 1917, he enlisted in the army and fought in World War I as an officer in the Battle of Somme. While hospitalized for shell shock, Owen wrote about the horror of battle. He died one year after returning to fight, and one week before the war ended, in 1918. He was awarded the Military Cross for serving in the war with distinction.

LINDA PASTAN has published many poetry collections, including *The Five Stages of Grief* and *Waiting for My Life.* Much of her poetry deals with her own family life and, more recently, with issues of aging and mortality.

OSCAR PEÑARANDA was born in the Philippines in 1944. His first language is Waray, and his second and third, Tagalog (on the streets), and English (in classrooms). He has taught at San Francisco State University for 25 years, where he co-founded the first ethnic studies program in the U.S. His work is anthologized in many publications, including the earliest collections of Asian and Filipino American writing.

PANDELIS PREVELAKIS has written over 20 books of novels, criticism, plays, and poetry, many of which have been translated into English, French, and German.

BUFFY SAINTE-MARIE became known in the 1960s as a writer of protest songs and love songs, many of which were performed by artists such as Janis Joplin, Elvis Presley, Barbra Streisand, Neil Diamond, and Tracy Chapman. She was recently awarded the Award for Lifetime Musical Achievement by the First Americans in the Arts (U.S.), which award was also named after her, as a tribute to her legendary career.

LUIS OMAR SALINAS'S poems, which often relate the problems of Mexican Americans, have won a number of awards.

NANCY SENIOR was born in 1941, and emigrated from the U.S. to Saskatoon in 1967. Her poetry collections include *Poems* (1973), and *The Mushroom Jar* (1980).

WILLIAM SHAKESPEARE was born in 1564, in Stratford-on-Avon, England. He composed over a hundred sonnets between 1593 and 1601. These were written in the form of three quatrains and a rhyming couplet, now recognized as the Shakespearean sonnet. He died in 1616.

PERCY BYSSHE SHELLEY was born in 1792 in Sussex, England. He began writing poetry while at Eton, but his first publication was a Gothic novel, *Zastrozzi*. Shelley produced all his major works during the last four years of his life, including *Prometheus Unbound*. In 1822, just before his thirtieth birthday, he was drowned in a storm while sailing in his schooner.

RAYMOND SOUSTER was born in 1921 and won many awards for his poetry: including a Governor General's Award for Poetry, the President's Medal, the Centennial Medal, and the Silver Jubilee Medal.

EDNA ST. VINCENT MILLAY, born in 1892, was a poet and playwright. In 1923, her fourth volume of poems, *The Harp Weaver*, was awarded the Pulitzer Prize.

SARA TEASDALE was born in St. Louis, Missouri., U.S. in 1884, and published her first volume of poetry in 1907. Further volumes followed and, in 1918, she won the Columbia University Poetry Society prize (forerunner of the Pulitzer Prize for poetry), and the annual prize of the Poetry Society of America for *Love Songs*. Teasdale died in 1933.

ALFRED, LORD TENNYSON, English poet of the Victorian age, was born in 1809, and succeeded William Wordsworth as Poet Laureate in 1850. His reputation as a poet was established in 1842 with his revised volume of *Poems*. In 1850, he published one of his major poetic works, "In Memoriam;" an elegy mourning the death of his friend, Arthur Hallam.

DYLAN THOMAS was born in Wales in 1914. Although he excelled in English and reading, he dropped out of school at 16. His first book—*Eighteen Poems*—was published to great acclaim when he was 20. He died in 1953 at the age of 39.

MIRIAM WADDINGTON was born in Winnipeg in 1917. She was the Canada Council Exchange Poet to Wales in 1980, and has been poetry editor of *Poetry Toronto*, and writer-in-residence at both the Windsor Public Library and the University of Ottawa.

MICHAEL WADE is a creative writer and accomplished musician, who published his first poem in 1972 in *Voices Underground* magazine. He lives in Nova Scotia and is working on a novel.

AGNES ETHELWYN WERTHERALD was born of English-Quaker parents in Ontario in 1857. She began to write poetry later in life. Her first book of verse, *The House of the Trees and Other Poems*, was published in 1895. She died in 1940.

CHRISTOPHER WISEMAN has taught English and Creative Writing at the University of Calgary, and has been editor of *Dandelion* and *Ariel*. Wiseman received Alberta Poetry awards in both 1988 and 1989.

WILLIAM WORDSWORTH was born in 1770 in England. Wordsworth's earliest poetry collections—*An Evening Walk* and *Descriptive Sketches*—were published in 1793. He died in 1850, and his most famous poem, "The Prelude," was published posthumously by his wife.

JUDITH WRIGHT, an Australian, wrote poetry, children's books, non-fiction, and short stories, and also worked as a literary critic, editor, anthologist, active conservationist, and supporter of Aboriginal land rights. Wright received numerous awards for her writing, including the Human Rights Commission Award for Poetry, in 1994. She died in June, 2000.

# Glossary

In the **active voice**, the subject of a sentence does the action: *The dog ran into the street.* Use the active voice when possible. It uses fewer words and is more precise than the passive voice. See **Passive Voice.**

An **allegory** is a simple story, such as a fable or parable, whose major purpose is to teach a moral lesson. An allegory can always be read on two levels—one literal, the other symbolic. The underlying meaning can be parallel to, but different from, the surface meaning.

An **allusion**, in a literary work, is a reference to another literary work, or a person, place, event, or object from history, literature, or mythology.

An **analogy** is the illustration of one idea or concept by using a similar idea or concept. An analogy is sometimes phrased as a simile.

The **antagonist** of a narrative or dramatic work is the primary person in opposition to the hero or **protagonist**.

An **archetype** is a theme, symbol, character, or setting that can be found throughout literature, folklore, and media so often that it comes to reflect some universal human character or experience. For example, Robin Hood is an archetypal hero.

**Assonance** (also known as *vowel rhyme*) is the repetition of similar or identical vowel sounds within the words of a poem or other writing.

**Beat writers** were a group of American writers from the 1950s, whose loose writing style was a form of self-expression, often accompanied by jazz music. Poet Lawrence Ferlinghetti was a major beat poet who strongly influenced later generations.

**Bias** is an inclination or preference that makes it difficult or impossible to judge fairly in a particular situation.

A **cacophony** is a harsh or clashing sound, often caused deliberately for effect.

A **caesura** is a pause in a line of verse, generally agreeing with a pause required by the sense.

**Climax** See **Plot.**

**Consonance** is the repetition of similar or identical consonants in words whose vowels differ. For example, *gripe/grape/grope.*

**Diction** refers to the way an author expresses ideas in words. Good diction includes grammatical correctness, skill in the choice of effective words, and a wide vocabulary.

A **dynamic character** is one who undergoes a significant and permanent change in personality or beliefs.

A **fact sheet** presents key information about a particular topic, issue, or organization. It provides concise answers to basic questions. Some fact sheets are written in point form, others in full sentences.

**Figurative language** uses words to paint a picture, draw an interesting comparison, or create a poetic effect. **Literal language** says what it means directly. Language can be figurative or literal.

**Free-verse** poetry is written without using regular rhyme or rhythm. Images, spacing, punctuation, and the rhythms of ordinary language are used to create a free-verse poem.

**Foreshadowing** is a plot technique in which a writer plants clues or subtle indications about events that will happen later in the narrative.

**Hyperbole** is a deliberately exaggerated statement made for effect.

**Imagery** is the pictures or impressions that writers create in the minds of their readers. To create these pictures, they use descriptive techniques such as figures of speech (simile, metaphor, personification, oxymoron), onomatopoeia, alliteration, and allusions.

**Irony** occurs when a statement or situation means something different from (or even the opposite of) what is expected. Another type of irony is **dramatic irony**. It occurs in plays when the audience knows something that the characters do not.

A **literary essay** presents an interpretation or explores some aspect of one or more works of literature.

A **loaded word** is a word intentionally chosen to evoke a strong response in a reader—usually an emotional response.

A **metaphor** is a comparison of two things that are not alike. The comparison suggests that they do share a common quality: *Her words were a knife to my heart*.

**Parallelism** is the intentional use of identical or similar grammatical structure within one sentence or in two or more sentences.

**Parallel structure** is the repeated use of the same phrase or sentence, or the repeated use of a similar sentence structure. Parallel structure can be used to create balance or place emphasis on certain lines.

In the **passive voice**, the subject of the verb receives the actions: *The fire was extinguished*.

**Personification** occurs when objects, ideas, or animals are given human qualities: *The sun smiled down on me.*

**Plot** refers to the events in a story. It usually has five elements: exposition, rising action, climax, falling action, and resolution.
- The **exposition** or introduction sets up the story by introducing the main characters, the setting, and the problem to be solved.
- The **rising action** is the main part of the story where the full problem develops. A number of events is involved that will lead to the climax.
- The **climax** is the highest point in the story where something decisive occurs.
- The **falling action** follows the climax. It contains the events that bring the story to its conclusion.
- The **resolution** or denouement is the end of the story and traces the final outcome of the central conflict.

A **point of view** is the vantage point from which the author tells a story. The four most common points of view are *first person* (I, me), *omniscient* (all-seeing), *limited omniscient* (all-seeing from the viewpoint of a group of characters), and *objective* (he, she, they, it).

A **précis** is a concise summary of a text. It is written in full sentences, but contains only the most important information.

**Racist language** is any language that refers to a particular cultural or ethnic group in insulting terms, but racism also exists in more subtle forms.
- Mention a person's race only if it is relevant to the context. If a person's race or ethnic origin is relevant, be specific:
  Irrelevant/Vague:      *Dago is African.*
  Relevant/Less Vague:   *Dago is proud of her Nigerian heritage.*
- Avoid making generalizations about any racial or cultural group:
  Stereotype:            *The Welsh are great singers.*
  Better:                *The Welsh have a long tradition of singing.*

**Resolution** See **Plot.**

A **rhetorical question** is one that is asked for effect, and that does not invite a reply. The purpose of a rhetorical question is to introduce a topic or to focus the reader on a concern.

**Rhythm** is the arrangement of beats in a line of poetry. The beat is created by the accented and unaccented syllables in the words used in each line.

A **satire** is a work that criticizes something—for example, a person, a characteristic, an institution, or a government—by depicting it in a humorous, sarcastic, or scornful way.

**Sexist language** is language that degrades or unnecessarily excludes either women or men. It is best to avoid generalizing about males and females unless the claims are based on scientific facts.

- Whenever possible, replace words such as *fireman*, *policeman*, and *man-made* with non-sexist alternatives such as *firefighter*, *police officer*, and *fabricated*.
- Avoid using the masculine pronouns *he, him,* or *his* to refer to both men and women.

A **stereotype** is an oversimplified picture, usually of a group of people, giving them all a set of characteristics, without consideration for individual differences.

**Suspense** is a feeling of tension, anxiety, or excitement resulting from uncertainty. An author creates suspense to keep readers interested.

**Style** is the overall texture of a piece of writing; the particular way in which the ideas are expressed. Style is made up of many elements including diction, figurative language, sentences, and tone.

A **symbol** is something that represents something else—for example, the lion can be a symbol of courage.

The **symbolic meaning** of a work is developed through the symbols that the author includes.

A **theme** is a central thesis or idea that is expressed directly or indirectly in a literary work.

The **thesis** of an essay is the main idea or argument that the author is attempting to prove.

**Tone** is the implied attitude of the writer toward the subject or the audience. Tone differs from mood, which describes the emotional feeling of the work more generally. The tone of a piece of work can be described, for example, as *angry*, *satiric*, *joyful*, or *serious*.

**Transition words** indicate relationships between ideas. Writers use them to suggest links between sentences or paragraphs.

# Index of Titles and Authors

# Acknowledgments

Every reasonable effort has been made to trace ownership of copyrighted material. Information that would enable the publisher to correct any reference or credit in future editions would be appreciated.

**12** "Mirror Image" by Lena Coakley. Reprinted by permission of the author. **21** "The Prospector's Trail" by Cathy Jewison. Reprinted with permission of the author. **39** "Love Must Not Be Forgotten" by Zhang Jie, translated by Gladys Yang, Chinese Literature Press, 24 Baiwanzhuang Rd., Beijing 10037, People's Republic of China. **52** "Saturday Climbing" from *What Can't Be Changed Shouldn't Be Mourned* by W. D. Valgardson. © 1990 by W. D. Valgardson. Published in Canada by Douglas & McIntyre. Reprinted by permission of the publisher. **61** "The Maiden Wiser Than the Tsar" from *World Tales: The Extraordinary Coincidence of Stories Told in All Times, in All Places* by Idries Shah, © 1979 by Technographia, S. A., and Harcourt, Inc., reprinted by permission of Harcourt, Inc. **78** "The Labrador Fiasco" by Margaret Atwood. © 1996 O. W. Toad, Ltd., first published in the United Kingdom by Bloomsbury Publishing. **90** "Snow" by Ann Beattie. Reprinted with the permission of Simon & Schuster from *Where You'll Find Me and Other Stories* by Ann Beattie. © 1986 by Irony & Pity. **94** "A Secret Lost in the Water" from *The Hockey Sweater and Other Stories* by Roch Carrier, translated by Sheila Fischman. © 1979 by House of Anansi Press. Reprinted by permission of Stoddart Publishing Co. Limited. **98** "The Pose" by Anwer Khan, translated by Muhammad Umar Memon, from *Domains of Fear and Desire: Urdu Stories*. Reprinted with permission. **117** "Brooms for Sale" by Thomas Raddall is reprinted with permission of Dalhousie University. **124** "The Liberation of Rome" by Robin Hemley from *Sudden Fiction (Continued)* edited by Robert Shapard and James Thomas. **135** "Soul-Catcher" by Louis Owens. Reprinted by permission of the author. **145** "Wilhelm" by Gabrielle Roy, translated by Harry L. Binsse. © Fonds Gabrielle Roy. **152** "He-y, Come on Ou-t" by Shinichi Hoshi, translated by Stanleigh Jones, from *The Best Japanese Fiction Stories* by John L. Apossolou and Martin H. Greenberg. Reprinted with permission. **165** "A Poet's Advice to Students." © 1958, 1965 by the Trustees of the E. E. Cummings Trust. © 1958, 1965 by George J. Firmage, from *A Miscellany Revised* by E. E. Cummings, edited by George J. Firmage. Used by permission of Liveright Publishing Corporation. **167** "Poetry Is ..." by Betty Lies. Reprinted with permission of the author. **168** "What You Are Doing Now" by Gary Hyland. Reprinted by permission of the author. **169** "How Beautifully Useless" by Raymond Souster is reprinted from *Collected Souster* by permission of Oberon Press. **172** "Calgary 2 am" from *Postcards Home: Poems New and Selected* by Christopher Wiseman. © 1988 Sono Nis Press, Victoria, BC. **173** "God's World" by Edna St. Vincent Millay. From *Collected Poems*, HarperCollins.© 1913, 1941 by Edna St. Vincent Millay. All rights reserved Reprinted by permission of Elizabeth Barnett, literary executor. **175** "Canadian Sunrise" written by Joan Besen. © 1998 Published by *Retsyo Songs (Socan)*/ Administered by *Bug*. All Rights Reserved. Used By Permission. **178** "As in the Beginning" by Mary di Michele. Reprinted with permission of the author. **183** "Not only marble, but the plastic toys" from *Making Cocoa for Kingsley Amis* by Wendy Cope. London: Faber and Faber Limited. **186** "To Make a Prairie" by Emily Dickinson from *The Collected Poems of Emily Dickinson* edited by Thomas H. Johnson, Cambridge Mass.: The Belknap Press of Harvard University Press, © 1951, 1955 by the President and Fellows of Harvard College. Reprinted by permission of the publishers and the Trustees of Amherst College. **187** "Writer's Block in the Computer Age" by Peggy Smith Krachun. Reprinted by permission of the author. **188** "A Spider Danced a Cosy Jig" by Irving Layton from *The Collected Poems of Irving Layton*. Used by permission of McClelland & Stewart, Ltd. *The Canadian Publishers*. **189** "Crazy Times" by Miriam Waddington. Don Mills: Oxford University Press Canada. **190** "Very Like a Whale" from *Verses From 1929 On* by Ogden Nash. London: Curtis Brown Limited. **194** "St. George" by Nancy Senior. Reprinted by permission of the author. **196** "The Unknown Citizen" by W. H. Auden from *Collected Poems of W. H. Auden* edited by Edward Mendelson. Reprinted by permission of Faber and Faber Limited. **197** "#9" by Lawrence Ferlinghetti, from *A Far Rockaway of the Heart*, © 1997 by Lawrence Ferlinghetti. Reprinted by permission of New Directions Publishing Corp. **199** "The Sunlight" by Chief Dan George. Reprinted by permission of

Hancock House Publishers. **200** "Universal Soldier" by Buffy Sainte-Marie. Reprinted with permission of the author. **201** "There Will Come Soft Rains" by Sara Teasdale. Reprinted with the permission of Scribner, a Division of Simon & Schuster, from *The Collected Poems of Sara Teasdale* (New York: Macmillan, 1937). **201** "I Believe" by Robert Fulghum from *It Was on Fire When I Lay Down on It* by Robert Fulghum. © 1988, 1989 by Robert Fulghum. Used by permission of Villard Books, a division of Random House, Inc. **202** "the laughing heart" by Charles Bukowski. © 1996 by Linda Lee Bukowski. Reprinted from *Betting on the Muse: Poems & Stories* with the permission of Black Sparrow Press. **203** "The Sun Witness" from *I See Cleopatra and Other Poems* translated by Nurunnessa Choudhury and Paul Joseph Thompson. London: Egmont Children's Books. **204** "Take Something Like a Star" from *The Poetry of Robert Frost* edited by Edward Connery Lathem. © 1949, 1969 by Henry Holt and Co., © 1977 by Lesley Frost Ballantine. Reprinted by permission of Henry Holt and Company, LLC. **208** "Hockey" by Scott Blaine from *Grab Me a Bus ... and Other Award Winning Poems* by Malcolm Glass and M. Joe Eaton. © 1971 by Scholastic Inc. Reprinted by permission of Scholastic Inc. **209** "The Rain Hammers" by Michael Wade from *Passages (Literature of Newfoundland and Labrador) Book 3*, Breakwater, St. John's, © 1980 Michael Wade. **211** "Prelude #1" from *Collected Poems 1909–1962* by T. S. Eliot. London: Faber and Faber Limited. **211** "The Spider Holds a Silver Ball" by Emily Dickinson from *The Collected Poems of Emily Dickinson* edited by Thomas H. Johnson, Cambridge, Mass.: The Belknap Press of Harvard University Press, © 1951, 1955 by the President and Fellows of Harvard College. Reprinted by permission of the publishers and the Trustees of Amherst College. **214** "Gaining Yardage" by Leo Dangel from *Home from the Field* (Spoon River Poetry Press, Granite Falls, Minnesota), © 1997 by Leo Dangel. **215** "Snake" by D. H. Lawrence from *The Complete Poems of D. H. Lawrence*. Reprinted with permission of Lawrence Pollinger Limited and the estate of Frieda Lawrence Ravagli. **219** "Legend" by Judith Wright from *A Human Pattern: Selected Poems* (ETT Imprint, Sydney © 1996). **220** "The Child Who Walks Backwards" by Lorna Crozier. Reprinted with permission of the author. **224** "This Morning I Sat" by Rosalie Fowler. Reproduced with permission of Breakwater, St. John's. © Rosalie Fowler. **226** "Nothing Is Like Nothing Else" by Elizabeth Brewster. Reprinted with permission of the author. **227** "The New House" by Maya Angelou from *I Shall Not Be Moved*. © 1990 by Maya Angelou. Reprinted by permission of Random House, Inc. **228** "Death of a Young Son by Drowning" by Margaret Atwood from *Selected Poems 1966-1984*. © 1990 Margaret Atwood. Reprinted by permission of Oxford University Press Canada. **229** "My Father Is a Simple Man" by Luis Omar Salinas from *The Sadness of Days: Selected and New Poems*. Reprinted with permission. **230** "Ethics" from *Waiting For My Life* by Linda Pastan. © 1981 by Linda Pastan. Used by permission of W. W. Norton & Company, Inc. **237** "A Bird Came Down" by Emily Dickinson from *The Collected Poems of Emily Dickinson* edited by Thomas H. Johnson, Cambridge, Mass.: The Belknap Press of Harvard University Press, © 1951, 1955 by the President and Fellows of Harvard College. Reprinted by permission of the publishers and the Trustees of Amherst College. **240** "Dulce Et Decorum Est" by Wilfred Owen from *The Collected Poems of Wilfred Owen*. © 1963 by Chatto & Windus, Ltd. Reprinted by permission of New Directions Publishing Corp. **241** "Harlem" by Langston Hughes from *The Collected Poems of Langston Hughes*. © 1994 by the estate of Langston Hughes. Used by permission of Alfred A. Knopf, a division of Random House, Inc.

**Visual Credits**
**11** Dave Robertson/Masterfile. **44** Andrew Hunter and Gu Xiong. **89** *Travelers* by Judith Currelly/Diane Farris Gallery, Vancouver. **92** *Illinois Farm* by Richard Hamilton Smith/The Image Works. **114** ©Bettmann/CORBIS. **133** Chris Alan Wilton/Image Bank. **163** *Rock painting, Zimbabwe,* Holton Collection/SuperStock. **174** *Spring Wind—Apollo Coast* by Paul Grignon, visit his Web site at www.paulgrignonart.com. **191** *Winter's Blanket #1* by David McEown, courtesy of the artist. **195** *St. George and the Dragon,* c.1460 Paolo Uccello (1397-1475) (oil on canvas), National Gallery, London, UK/The Bridgeman Art Library International Ltd. **210** Harald Sund/Image Bank. **218** Marilyn Conway/Image Bank. **231** Réunion des Musées Nationaux/Art Resource, NY.